LILI
PROSE POEMS A

"RENÉE VIVIEN" (Pauline Mary Tarn, 1877-1909) was introduced into Symbolist circles by one of her lovers, Natalie Barney, but produced the bulk of her work while in a relationship with Hélène de Zuylen de Nyevelt, with whom she collaborated on a number of books under the pseudonym Paule Riversdale. Under her usual pseudonym she published two volumes of prose poems and two further volumes of prose as well as the numerous volumes of poetry that helped to make her notorious as a kind of tragic symbolic embodiment of the Belle Époque: a neurotic, anorexic, alcoholic, suicidal lesbian doomed to self-destruction.

BRIAN STABLEFORD has been publishing fiction and non-fiction for fifty years. His fiction includes an eighteen-volume series of "tales of the biotech revolution" and a series of half a dozen metaphysical fantasies set in Paris in the 1840s, featuring Edgar Poe's Auguste Dupin. His most recent non-fiction projects are *New Atlantis: A Narrative History of British Scientific Romance* (Wildside Press, 2016) and *The Plurality of Imaginary Worlds: The Evolution of French* roman scientifique (Black Coat Press, 2016); in association with the latter he has translated approximately a hundred and fifty volumes of texts not previously available in English, similarly issued by Black Coat Press.

Renée Vivien

LILITH'S LEGACY
PROSE POEMS AND SHORT STORIES

Translated and with an Introduction by
Brian Stableford

THIS IS A SNUGGLY BOOK

ISBN: 978-1-943813-63-6

Contents

Introduction

THIS is the first of three volumes translating prose works by Pauline Mary Tarn (1877-1909); it contains all the shorter works signed with her best-known pseudonym, originally "R. Vivien" and subsequently "Renée Vivien." The second volume, *Faustina and Other Stories*, will contain stories that were originally signed Paule Riversdale—a pseudonym used jointly by Pauline Tarn and Baroness Héléne van Zuylen van Nijevelt van de Haar (née Hélène de Rothschild, 1863-1947)—and some of those that appeared under the French version of the latter signature, but which are believed to be at least partly Tarn's work. The third volume will contain the two longer works entitled *Une Femme m'apparut* that Tarn published as Renée Vivien in 1904 and 1905 respectively, which are too dissimilar to be considered merely as a single work that underwent revision between editions.

The prose poems in the first part of this collection were first published by Alphonse Lemerre in 1902 as *Brumes de fjords*, signed R. Vivien. Those in the second section were first published by Lemerre in 1903 as *Du Vert au Violet*, signed Renée Vivien. The stories in the third section were published by Lemerre in 1904 as *La Dame à la Louve*, signed Renée Vivien, and the final two stories in *Le Christ,*

Aphrodite et M. Pépin, signed Renée Vivien, published by Edward Sansot in 1907.

Brumes de Fjords was the fourth book by Pauline Tarn that Lemerre published, following three volumes of poetry. *Du Vert au Violet* was the seventh, following a fourth collection of poetry and *Sapho*, a volume of "translations and adaptations" of the work of the Dorian poet. The first four volumes were all signed "R. Vivien" but when the first two were sent out to potential reviewers a compliment slip was enclosed expanding that name as "René Vivien," although the second *e* was added to the compliment slip enclosed with the second and third volumes, after which the signature Renée Vivien was rendered in full on the title pages.

A further collection of poems bearing the full signature, another volume of translations and adaptations, and two volumes of prose followed in 1904, and one more volume of poems in 1906. Meanwhile, in 1903-4 Lemerre also published four volumes under the joint pseudonym Paule Riversdale, including the short story collection *Netsuké*. Some commentators—including Jean-Paul Goujon, who argues to that effect in *Tes Blessures sont plus douces que leurs caresses, vie de Renée Vivien* [Your wounds are sweeter than their caresses; A Biography of Renée Vivien] (1986)—believe that the Paule Riversdale titles were almost entirely the work of Tarn. Lemerre also issued two volumes of prose fiction signed "Hélène de Zuylen de Nyevelt"—the author used the French version of her name in her publications—which Goujon also believes to be mostly Tarn's work. Examination of the stories in the collections *Netsuké* and *Copeaux* and comparison with those translated in the present volume suggests that Goujon's judgment is probably correct with regard to the short stories; some of the stories might well be entirely Tarn's work, and even those that might be mostly or entirely the work of Hélène de Zuylen are obviously very heavily influenced by Tarn.

The London-born Pauline Tarn received her early education in Paris, but following the sudden death of her father—a rich playboy passionate about horse-racing—in 1886 she mostly lived in London, where she felt badly neglected by her mother, occasioning a lifelong rancor that extended to outright hatred but was occasionally subject to necessary compromise, mainly because Pauline was very fond of her younger sister Antoinette, who lived with her mother until she married in 1907.

Pauline was eventually able to return to Paris for good in the late 1890s, where she soon met the American socialite Natalie Barney, who was her lover from 1899-1901. The two lived together for a while, but the relationship was always deeply troubled by Tarn's jealousy of Barney's other lovers, until she broke it off while Barney was away in America. Tarn then began a long relationship with Hélène de Zuylen—who, conveniently, lived almost opposite her new residence, on the other side the Avenue de Bois. Their affair was conducted in secret; Hélène de Zuylen was married, and Pauline Tarn attempted to keep her lesbianism—and her writing—secret from her family and from the greater part of Paris society.

Another near neighbor of Pauline Tarn's during the last few years of her life was Colette, with whom she formed an amity of sorts, albeit one afflicted by her inveterate secrecy. Colette included an account of her friendship with "Renée Vivien" in a set of reminiscences she published in serial form as *Le Pur et l'impur* in 1931-32 and reprinted as *Ces plaisirs* . . . (1932) before an expanded and definitive version was published under the original title in 1941. The factual accuracy of the portrait was challenged by Natalie Barney and others, but there is no reason to doubt its sincerity, and if Colette was mistaken regarding Tarn's true character, she was surely deliberately misled by Tarn herself, for reasons that are unclear. Colette represents "Renée Vivien" as a strange, rather poignant figure, physically very attractive and always laughing, but eccentric, neurotic, alcoholic, given to paranoid fantasies—or at least to fantasization—and potentially suicidal; there is also mention in the portrait of a peculiar relationship with food, which has led some commentators to suggest that Tarn might have been anorexic as well.

Colette records that Pauline Tarn often gave her copies of her books as they were published, but always hid them under a bunch of violets or some other gift, and that seems to have been emblematic of the life she led, the greater part of it always kept hidden, at least in a tokenistic fashion. Her lesbianism, however, always known to her close acquaintances, gradually became common knowledge, and eventually led, by 1905 or thereabouts, to a partial ostracism in some sectors of the stratum of Parisian society in which she had previously moved freely, somewhat to her distress—not so much on her own account as because of potential embarrassment to her sister if the gossip spread to London.

The determinedly perverse obsession with death exhibited by Vivien's literary work certainly helps to endorse Colette's opinion of her neurotic and self-destructive tendencies, and although she did not actually commit suicide, the fact that she seems to have spent the last month of her life stubbornly isolated, in a room filled with exotic *objects d'art* whose curtains were never opened, poorly illuminated by candlelight, does suggest a certain degree of collaboration with the disease that actually brought about her premature death. Colette's judgment of her attractiveness is also endorsed, however, by the fact that Natalie Barney tried repeatedly to renew their relationship after it broke down, indulging in a fervent contest for her affection with Hélène de Zuylen until the despairing Tarn broke with both of them—although they both seem to have made serious efforts to remain close to her and both showed anxious concern for her declining welfare.

Reading between the lines of Colette's account with the benefit of informed hindsight, the picture that emerges from it is very clearly that of someone who was deeply confused and conflicted, not only by the fact that she felt obliged to hide much of her life and her self, but because she really did not know what she wanted to make of that life and that self, beyond her passionate vocation as a writer. In fact, circumstances left her with very little freedom of movement in any other regard, and she seems to have felt trapped in a series of no-win situations. That, too, is an impression that comes across very strongly in Vivien's writing, and can surely be regarded as one of its principal guiding forces.

Jean-Paul Goujon suggests, on the basis of his detailed and scrupulous observation of all the material he could gather about Pauline Tarn's life, that what she desperately wanted was a secure and stable relationship with a female lover who would also fill the protective maternal gap that her appalling mother had left vacant. He might well be correct in his opinion that she would have had a happier life if she had actually found something of that sort, but the evidence that she actually wanted it, for more than a few days at a time, is slim, and any judgment that it was what she needed remains necessarily speculative. The evidence of her life and her works alike suggests very strongly that she could never make up her mind what she wanted, what she ought to want, and what—if anything—might help her to be happy.

Goujon's evidence suggests that Tarn did not even know for certain whether she wanted to be a lesbian, in spite of the fervent propagandizing in favor of that state of being that features in some of her poetry and prose. All her writings about Sappho—whom she preferred to call Psappha, that being the Dorian form of the name—are admiring, even more for her presumed sexuality than her poetry, but it is possible that she could never put it out of her mind that Sappho was alleged to have committed suicide, and could not rid herself of the idea that sapphism might be intrinsically essentially fatal.

"R. Vivien's" early work was inevitably likened to the poetry of the Symbolist and Decadent Movements, although Pauline Tarn probably took little direct influence from the Movement's contemporary writers, the strong similarities between her work and theirs being the result of common influences, most obviously that of Baudelaire. Charles Maurras, who wrote an extensive critical appreciation of Vivien's work, along with that of three other female poets, in a long essay on *Le Romanticisme féminin* (1922; reprinted in the collection *L'Avenir de l'intelligence*, 1927), described her as the most Baudelairean of all that poet's many successors, and that influence extended to her strong interest in prose poetry as well as her attempted refinement of what Théophile Gautier characterized as Baudelaire's "decadent style," and the frequent morbidity of his themes.

In considering the Symbolist and Decadent elements in Vivien's work, however, the most vital factor determining their use and pattern is the fact that when she is writing about her own feelings and aspects of her own life—as she did, relentlessly—she always felt obliged to mask what she was doing by means of methodical transfiguration. If she is, in some respects, one of the most extreme writers in the Symbolist vein, that is because much of what she was symbolizing was so deeply personal and so awkwardly problematic that it could only be represented publicly in intricately veiled terms. Her writing was, in large measure, part and parcel of her attempt to grapple with her personal problems, dramatizing aspects of her predicaments, trying to glimpse the possibility of solutions—or at least figure out what sort of a solution she wanted to find—and, most of all, trying to estimate the likely outcome of the various pressures acting upon her. In the last regard, her work is far from optimistic, but how could it be otherwise? What hope could she have possibly discovered, other than the one she harked back to repeatedly: the hope that death might not, after all, be that bad, and in any case preferable to life?

Given Renée Vivien's existential situation, therefore, it is not in the least surprising that almost all of the items in the present collection and its companions are quintessential exercises in Decadent Symbolist prose. Some of the stories employ a typical *fin-de-siècle* method of hybridization, which fused the Baudelairean tradition of prose poetry with imitation folktales that deliberately mutated "tales of enchantment" into mordant tales of disenchantment. In terms of the extent of her disenchantment, Vivien had few rivals among the self-proclaimed Symbolists, none of whom had the full set of her existential disadvantages, although Jean Lorrain came as close as any male writer could, and his reconstituted folktales, studies in perverse psychology and brief accounts of "*moeurs antiques*" all have something in common with some of the items herein and some of those in the companion volumes.

The prose-poems in *Brumes de fjords*, published at the very beginning of Vivien's relationship with Hélène de Zuylen, and probably written before it began, at a time when "R. Vivien" had not yet admitted to being female, let alone lesbian, employ a very vague and somewhat inconsistent narrative viewpoint, although disguised references to Vivien's feelings regarding Natalie Barney are easily detectable with the aid of hindsight. There is a marked evolution between the items in the earlier collection and the prose poems in *Du Vert au Violet*, where it is generally obvious that the narrative viewpoint is female, and deliberately perverse; "Lilith," the first item in *Du Vert au Violet* takes over directly from the last item in *Brumes de fjords* "Le Genèse profane" (tr. as "The Profane Genesis"), and the two, seen in combination, seem to represent a deliberate and resolute step. The last five items in *Brumes de fjords* had already been separated out from the previous ones as "Part Two" of the collection, only the first twelve echoing the title, and being identified on the contents page, falsely, as translations of Norwegian poems.

The items in the second collection are considerably broader in scope, and although lesbian themes are more common and more assertive therein, it is worth noting that that would not have been sufficient in itself to inform readers of the sexuality of the author, literary lesbianism already having a long history, most of it romanticized by male writers from Baudelaire to Pierre Louÿs. There is nothing paradoxical about the fact that Pauline Tarn thought that she could publish such material without necessarily giving herself away, and thinking that her secret could still be kept from her family, and perhaps from Hélène de Zuylen's family too.

Although the third collection translated here, *La Dame à la louve*, appeared in the same year as the Paule Riversdale collection *Netsuké* and Hélène de Zuylen de Nyevelt's *Copeaux*, the order in which the stories in the three collections were written is unclear, and their composition surely overlapped to a considerable degree. The stories in the first section of *Netsuké* have a marked continuity with the earlier collections of prose poems, so the temptation is to conclude that it mostly consists of earlier work than either of the other two volumes, but that is certainly not true of the stories in the final section. A similar argument might lead one to suspect that the work in *La Dame à la louve* was mostly later than the work assembled in *Copeaux*, but however the sequence is imagined, the earlier items in *La Dame à la louve* certainly mark a very dramatic break in the pattern, and constitute a remarkable series of narrative experiments.

It is not so very uncommon for female writers to adopt male first-person viewpoints, nor is it entirely surprising that, when they do, it is sometimes in the interests of creating an unsympathetic narrator, but there are few examples of calculated misandry as caustic as Vivien's, and perhaps no others that display such extreme contrasts between the horrid male narrators featured in *La Dame à la louve* and the heroic women after whom they sometimes lust so hopelessly. The best of the stylishly discomfiting group of stories that begins the collection—including the title story (tr. as "The She-Wolf Lady"), and "La Saurienne" (tr. as "The Saurienne")—are highly unusual and very striking. "Cruauté des pierreries" (tr. as "The Cruelty of Precious Stones") is the odd one out in the set, but is equally effective in its portrayal of its despicable narrator, and perhaps even more calculatedly perverse in giving him the upper hand over a female antagonist who is certainly no angel.

The autobiographical novel *Une Femme m'apparut* [A Woman Appeared to Me] also appeared in 1904, its publication dated 22 February, and thus preceding the collections, although much the material assembled in the collections was probably written before it. In any case, the author produced a new and considerably different version in 1905, which justifies its separate and subsequent publication in this series of translations. Those two texts, and the alterations made between the two versions, demonstrate very clearly indeed the difficulty that Vivien was having in clarifying her attitude to those lovers and to herself.

Une Femme m'apparut is, unsurprisingly, the most explicitly and extravagantly lesbian of all Pauline Tarn's works, but it is worth noting that the final item in *La Dame à la louve*, "Bona Dea," is similarly forthright, and so are three of the stories in the final section of *Netsuké*. If, as seems likely, "Bona Dea" was the last item in *La Dame à la louve* to be written, and the items in the final section of *Netsuké* were also the last of that collection's inclusions to be written, the group as a whole might have signaled a new change in direction, toward a much greater frankness. If that was ever an intention, however, it appears to have been aborted, and after the remarkable flood of prose published by Tarn and Zuylen in 1904, there was then something of a drought, in which the second version of *Une Femme m'apparut* was a lonely oasis.

The only two subsequent works of original prose published during Pauline Tarn's lifetime were two brief satires written for periodical publication before being reprinted in the exceedingly thin volume *Le Christ, Aphrodite et M. Pépin*. While certainly interesting, insofar as they testify to yet another change of direction and method, they are also rather insubstantial and uneasy, and probably illustrate all too clearly the fact that the author's prodigious alcohol consumption and increasingly chaotic personal life had severely undermined her ability to work effectively by 1907. They do, however, help to demonstrate the remarkable range of her work, and to emphasize the tragedy that a career with so much potential was cut brutally short.

It is as much by virtue of her idiosyncrasies as because of her considerable, if somewhat inconsistent, artistry that Pauline Tarn/Renée Vivien was, and remains, an extremely interesting writer. She did, however, have the rare privilege of combining a very considerable technical skill and intellectual brilliance with a vivid and versatile imagination and a literary standpoint that was unique in its day. That standpoint remains unusual even now, although historical circumstances have become much more hospitable to its potential appreciation in the last quarter of a century. Her poetry, inevitably, can only be properly appreciated in its original language, but her prose translates very well, as the present collection and its companions will hopefully demonstrate, and it is certainly more likely to find a sympathetic and understanding audience today than ever before.

The translation of *Brumes de fjords* was made from the *Wikisource* version of the text available on-line. The translation of *Du Vert au Violet* was made from the London Library's copy of the Lemerre edition. The translations of *La Dame à la Louve* and *Le Christ, Aphrodite et M. Pépin* were made from the copies of the original editions reproduced on the Bibliothèque Nationale's *gallica* website.

—Brian Stableford

LILITH'S LEGACY

PROSE POEMS AND SHORT STORIES

FJORD MISTS

The Winds

AS I was going toward the hill I encountered the North Wind.

He was clad in a large cloak of snow and his crown of icicles was sparkling.

He said to me: "Let me take you away to the immutable whiteness. You will see incomparable aurorae, immobile and luminous seas, mountains of crystal that float on the waters, and pale solitudes in the depths of the eternal silence."

I replied to the North Wind:

My soul is retained in the village by the indecisive smile of a virgin.

The North Wind fled in a flutter of wings.

As I was going toward the hill I encountered the East Wind.

He was clad in purple and his crown of radiance was flamboyant.

He said to me: "Let me take you away to the light. You will see the sumptuousness of colors, the gilt of pagodas with bizarre bell-towers, the silky sheen of the robes of mousmés and the glorious birth of the Sun."

I replied to the East Wind:

My soul is retained in the village by the indecisive smile of a virgin.

The East Wind fled in a flutter of wings.

As I was going toward the hill I encountered the South Wind.

He was clad in gold and his crown of stars was resplendent.

He said: "Let me take you away to the azure. You will see forests of paradoxical vegetation, the grace of lionesses and the subtlety of panthers, indolent and splendid reptiles, temples and ruins, sphinxes crouching in deserts, oases and mirages, and the inexpressible magnificence of flowers."

I replied to the South Wind:

My soul is retained in the village by the indecisive smile of a virgin.

As I was going toward the hill I encountered the West Wind.

He was clad in pale green and his crown of pearls was radiant.

He said: "Let me take you away to the sea. You will see the infinity of streaming horizons and the mystical charm of mists, the passage of sails whose light whiteness is colored, toward dusk, with violet and orange, and the fabulous extent of Oceans."

I replied to the West Wind:

My soul is retained in the village by the indecisive smile of a virgin.

The West Wind fled in a flutter of wings.

The Black Swan

OVER the heavy waves, a flock of bright swans floated.

They left a silver reflection in their wake.

Seen from afar, they resembled undulating snow.

But one day they perceived a black swan, whose strange aspect destroyed the harmony of their assembled whiteness.

It had a plumage of mourning and its beak was a bloody red.

The swans were frightened by their singular companion.

Their terror became hatred, and they attacked the black swan so furiously that it nearly died.

And the black swan said to itself: "I am weary of the cruelty of my fellows, who are not my peers.

"I am weary of sly intimations and declared angers.

"I shall flee forever through the vast solitudes.

"I shall take off and I shall fly toward the sea,

"I shall know the taste of the bitter breezes of the open sea and the sensualities of the tempest.

"The tumultuous waves will lull my sleep, and I shall repose in the storm.

"The lightning will be my mysterious sister and the thunder my beloved brother."

It took off and flew toward the sea.

The peace of the fjords did not retain it, and it was not slowed down by the unreal reflections of trees and grass in the water; it disdained the austere immobility of the mountains.

It heard the distant rhythm of the waves.

But one day, a storm surprised it, brought it down and broke its wings.

The black swan understood obscurely that it was going to die without having seen the sea.

And yet, it scented the odor of the sea in the air.

The wind brought it a taste of salt and the aphrodisiac perfume of algae . . .

Its broken wings lifted it up in one last surge of amour.

And the wind carried its cadaver toward the sea.

Lamentation

FREYA the Goddess has disappeared
     She once came at the dawn of spring.
She is the incarnation of the beauty of the Universe.
Her hair is the sad gold of autumn foliage.
Her eyes are as green and blue as the fjords
Her flesh is whiter than moonlight over the mysterious
snow on mountain peaks.
Her veins are like rivers.
Her robe has the rhythm of waves.
She is the incarnation of the beauty of the Universe.
Freya the Goddess once arrived at the dawn of spring.
She came from the distant sea. A flock of seagulls
preceded her, and the wind from the sea followed in her
footsteps.
The clouds saw her pass by. And the clouds were re-
splendent, the clouds were dressed in gold and roses.
The mountains saw her pass by. They were adorned
with heather and thyme, eglantines and gentians.
The trees saw her pass by. They were constellated with
flowers and foliage.
The birds saw her pass by. They sang in the sunlight.
But immortal Freya has disappeared.
She disappeared in the twilight.

She came from the sea.

She departed toward the sea.

The seagulls followed her toward the distant sea.

Freya the Goddess has disappeared.

She will return in the dawn of a future spring.

When she reappears, the earth will shudder with delight.

When she smiles, people will be consoled.

She will bring the happiness for which everyone searches eternally, justice, opulence amour and peace.

Freya the goddess has disappeared.

For days without number, people have been waiting for her with tears, moans and gasps.

They await her with prayers and lamentations, begging her to reappear and smile at them, in order that they can be happy forever, in order that they can be consoled forever.

The Beggar-Woman

THE most beautiful of the daughters of Norway was a beggar-woman who begged on the highways . . .

She had eyes as blue as distances, ashen like the dusk, as violet as the shadow of trees and as green as April.

For the color of her eyes changed in accordance with the color of her thoughts.

The most beautiful of the daughters of Norway was a beggar-woman who begged on the highways . . .

She obtained profit from the whiteness of her skin, and prostituted herself to all those who passed along the road.

It happened that someone praised the beauty of that woman before the King.

The King summoned her to appear before him, but she did not respond to his summons, because she loved the dust and the wind of the highways.

The King had her brought by force, and she came, weeping, because she loved the dust and the wind of the highways.

Her hair was as flamboyant as autumn and the setting sun.

The King put the pale gold of a crown on her red hair.

The beggar-woman and prostitute became the glorious Queen.

One day, the Queen said to her young servants:

"My head is weary of bearing the weight of the crown.

"Once the wind of the highways blew in my hair . . .

"My bare feet were impregnated with the perfume of meadows.

"I slept amid the warmth of mown hay, and my lips knew the infinity of kisses that were never similar . . .

"Once the wind of the highways blew in my hair . . .

"And the beggars and the thieves and the shepherds fought over my caresses and murdered one another by night because of me.

"The azure was my palace, and the sun was my crown . . .

"Once the wind of the highways blew in my hair . . ."

And when night fell, she slid out of the royal bed and fled to the highways.

For a long time they searched for her in the depths of solitudes and ravines, and they found her body under cornflowers and daisies.

One of her lovers of the highways had cut her throat during the night.

They left her amid the mown hay.

The wind of the highways blew in her hair . . .

Around her floated the perfume of meadows.

The Dead

Iplucked the mysterious flower that takes root in the hearts of the dead.

I took away the funereal lamp that burns on tombs, and I penetrated all the way to the domain of the Dead, in order to obtain from them the secret of their forgetfulness of things, and of their enviable peace.

A virgin was asleep in an ivory coffin.

She was asleep in a poor slumber, which was not traversed by the shadow of a dream. She was asleep, very white, in an ivory coffin. I touched her lips with the mysterious flower that takes root in the hearts of the dead, and the dead woman spoke in a languid voice:

"I am sleeping dreamlessly under the perfumed earth, because I have not known amour."

And her lips fell silent, smiling.

A king was buried in a golden coffin. I touched his lips with the mysterious flower, and the king replied to me:

"I am sleeping happily under the earth. I have known the din of assaults, the sonority of clarions and battle cries, the tread of armies, the ardent anguish of conflicts and the glory of victory; I have known omnipotence, pride and limitless splendor, and the glory of a crown.

"But I have not known amour, and that is why I am sleeping without regret under the earth."

A prophet was asleep in an ebony coffin. I touched his lips with the mysterious flower, and the prophet replied to me:

"I am sleeping peacefully under the earth. I know the secret of spaces and numbers, oceans and dawns. I have interrogated the stars and the silence, I have sounded the frightful universe resolutely, I have confronted the horror of the unknown, I have leaned over abysms and I have plunged into darkness.

"But today I am sleeping peacefully under the earth, for I have not known amour."

And I saw the tortured face of a dead man who was only half-asleep, oppressed by a nightmare. I touched his lips with the mysterious flower.

He groaned, in a pain-racked voice:

"I do not know warm slumber under the earth. The Dead, my neighbors, sleep divinely. Sometimes, they turn over on their serene couches. The soil that covers them is like perfumed velvet. They listen obscurely to the veiled sounds of the existence that no longer afflicts them.

"They sense the effort of plants germinating, sprouting, growing and flowering toward the distant sun. They divine the breath of the wind in the grass, and the odor of violets in the shade, and the melancholy clarities of evening slip all the way to their solitude and mingle with their dream . . .

"The Dead, my neighbors, sleep happily. But I am eternally unquiet, for I have known amour . . .

"I am suffering from the beauty of a woman. I have hated her voluptuously and loved her bitterly. Her caresses had the charm of a peril and the inadmissible attraction of a treason. Because of her, I have known intoxication and dolor.

"The Dead, my neighbors, sleep happily, but I am eternally unquiet, because I have known amour."

14

The Undine

ONE autumn evening, I saw the Undine smiling in the depths of the fjords.[1]

Her voice trickled in the warm silence.

"Give me roses, roses for my hair. My hair is like the reflection of moonlight on the water. Give me roses for my hair."

I collected the eglantines that whitened the valleys, and I strewed them on the water.

"And what will you give me in exchange for my roses?"

"I will not give you anything."

One autumn evening, I saw the Undine smiling in the depths of the fjords.

"Give me fruits for the feast of the Sirens and the Drowned. They move slowly and their movements have the rhythm of the tides. Their soul is like a conch in which the eddies of the sea vibrate eternally. They do not remember any amour."

I collected the wild berries that reddened the mountain, and I strewed them over the waves.

---

1 This item carried an individual dedication in the Lemerre text "To the Undine." We can, of course, only speculate as to who that might have been, but the probability is that it was intended to refer to Natalie Barney.

"Will you not give me something in exchange for the fruits of the mountain?"

"Do not hope for anything from me. I am the One who never gives. But rather, throw into my extended hands the gold necklace that a beloved person once brought you; for the Drowned are appearing to me in the depths of the mist, and their imploring gestures are inviting me to the feast . . ."

I took off the gold necklace and scattered it over the waves.

"Give me your eyes, in order that your gaze will never be stolen by any other vision of beauty . . . for the Drowned are appearing to me in the mist and their imploring gestures are inviting me to the feast."

I plucked out my eyes, which sank to the bottom of the waves.

"Give me your soul, in order that you will be similar to the Drowned, my lovers, who do not remember any other human tenderness . . ."

And my soul sank into the waves.

I cried out in the mist: "Will you not give me anything in exchange for my immortal soul?"

"I will give you nothing."

The Two Amours

I

A shepherd was wandering along a road skirting the abyss.

The mist was blurring the mountains and the solitudes were drinking the dusk, when he saw the Form of his Dream advancing.

Her face was pale through her veils. She had the smile of the amorous dead.[1]

And the Shade said to him: "Will you follow me to the realm of the Shades? You will reign at my side over an eternally beautiful people."

The mist was blurring the mountains and the solitudes were drinking the dusk.

In the depths of the evening, the distant faces of Shades were smiling.

But the shepherd replied to the Form of his Dream:

"I am marrying my fiancée tomorrow. Her eyes are as troubled as the glaciers. As for you, I have not been able

---

1 I have translated *mortes amoureuses* straightforwardly as "amorous dead," but "La Morte amoureuse" is the title of one of the most famous of Théophile Gautier's short stories, where it refers to a female vampire, and that association was almost certainly in the mind of the author.

to glimpse the color of your eyes. Her lips have the wild freshness of the roses in the valleys. I have not been able to glimpse the mystery of your lips. And her virginal flesh is like the snows warmed by spring. I have not been able to glimpse the unknown of your flesh.

"I am marrying my fiancée tomorrow."

The mist was blurring the mountains and the solitudes were drinking the dusk.

II

He resumed the road that skirted the abyss.

He was not able to forget the Form of his Dream.

The caresses of the bride left him a vulgar aftertaste.

He resumed the road that shirted the abyss . . .

And the amorous Shade was waiting for him in the twilight.

She said to him: "O you who cannot choose, you who hesitate eternally, will you follow me without fear into the reality of the dream?"

And the shepherd replied to the Form of his Dream:

"I dare not abandon forever the land of the living. I cannot abandon the Bride forever. But in the twilight hour I will descend with you into the realm of the Shades, and I will love you there for an hour."

III

Gone astray in the mist and deceived by the twilight, one of the living is smitten with a phantom.

In the twilight hour, the shepherd descended with the mystical Lover into the realm of the Shades, where even the roses are strangely pallid, where the birds no longer sing, where lips no longer kiss, but where the reflections, more beautiful than the colors and the echoes, and softer than the sounds, never collide with the idleness of the Dream.

Gone astray in the mist and deceived by the twilight, one of the living is smitten with a phantom.

For an hour, he was King in the realm of the Shades.

The crystal throne encrusted with emeralds illuminated the banqueting hall.

On the ground, round walls of ivory, among cups and ewers, flowers of snow were spread.

Beside the veiled Form, the shepherd thought, with melancholy, that the wines of the royal feast did not accord any intoxication, and that the lips of the amorous Shades were unaware of kisses. He remembered the embraces of his wife, being one of those who cannot choose, one of those who hesitate eternally.

The mist was blurring the mountains, and the solitudes were drinking the dusk.

The Rivals

I have known souls without repose whose thought remains among the living.

In a village in Nordfjord, two men hated one another with a profound hatred; for their wealth was equal and they had been rivals since childhood.

The sound of their quarrels saddened the evening.

Shrouded in the veils of dusk, Death descended into the village. She appeared to one of the rivals and took him away by the route of snows without April.

The survivor rejoiced and sat down at the banqueting table; and the dawn did not dissipate his drunkenness. He held happiness in the palm of his hand.

His domain expanded, his treasures accumulated, he loved and was loved.

The woman he loved and by whom he was loved was brighter than a stream in spring; in her eyes, the violet shadow of ferns on the mountains was visible. A virgin, she was in love for the first time.

The bright dawn of the marriage approached.

But the dead man was silently keeping watch on his rival. He lay in wait for him in the silence of the roads. He had not respired the lilies of the tombs, whose perfume gives forgetfulness. He was only half-asleep in the consoling warmth of the earth. And from the depths of the eternal solitudes, he beckoned to his rival.

At the dead man's summons, the living man was chilled.

I have known souls without repose whose thought remains among those they have hated or whom they have loved.

And the living man fell ill mysteriously.

Mysteriously, he went toward the roads of snows without April; for, from the depths of the eternal solitudes, the dead man had beckoned to him; the dead man had called to him by his name.

I have known souls without repose whose thought remains among the living.

The Human City

ONE day, a shepherd surprised the labor of the trolls. The trolls toil relentlessly during the night. They set immense furnaces ablaze, they make flames rise up and hiss therein, and they throw gold and rubies into them; for they hope to forge a glimmer of dawn.

The trolls toil relentlessly by night.

The shepherd said to the laborious trolls: "Why are you agitating thus in the darkness?"

And the trolls replied: "We do not know."

The shepherd said to the laborious trolls: "Your labor will never give rise to any glimmer of dawn, and you are weary of toiling in the night. Quit your anvils and your heavy hammers and climb up toward the sun.

"The morning wind is blowing through the wheat. The poppies are reddening the moist grass, and the sky is reflecting the depths of the luminous fjords.

"You are weary of toiling in the night. Your labor will never give rise to any glimmer of dawn. Quit your anvils and your heavy hammers and climb up toward the sun."

The trolls replied to him: "We do not know the road that leads to the sun. Leave us to our labor in the night."

And the shepherd said, one last time: "Why are you obstinate in your eternally vain task?"

And the trolls replied to him: "We do not know."

The trolls toil relentlessly during the night.

The Old Woman

IN the heart of the valley there is a pool that is called the Mysterious Pool.

On the black waters, no reed has ever quivered, and no nenuphar has ever flowered.

It is called the Mysterious Pool because it is unfathomable and terrible.

No one had ever reached its bottom, when the most audacious man in the surrounding villages resolved to discover the secret. He plunged into the opaque water, where even the wind came to vanish without ever stirring a ripple. He plunged into the abyss of which no one had ever reached the bottom.

For three days and three nights he fell vertiginously in the void.

Finally, he perceived a glimmer of dawn; and he entered into the light.

Above him, the black water swirled.

The man was in a garden where the flowers revealed strange designs and unknown breaths to him.

A lily had the form of a star, a rose burned like the sun.

Amid the universal beauty, an old woman was crouching. She displayed cynically the hideousness of moles and toads. Stooped, she seemed to be buckling under the weight of centuries. She was staring at the intruder with her extinct eyes. In truth, she had the hideousness of moles and toads.

And she said to him: "I know all the secrets of amour."

The man turned away, gripped by disgust.

But she went on: "I know all sensualities."

The man pushed her away with horror.

But she said to him: "Beauty pales before my omnipotence; for I know all sensualities."

And she kissed him on the mouth.

She had the hideousness of moles and toads.

But the man returned her kiss . . .

The most audacious of men never reappeared in his village. He lives forever enchained by a monstrous embrace . . .

In the hollow of the valley, there is a pool that is called the Mysterious Pool.

The Peevish Wife

THE village miller had married the daughter of a farmer.

She had pale blue eyes, but her mouth was twisted by a malevolent crease.

The miller's marriage was darkened by misfortune, because his wife was peevish and jealous. Her words swirled like the wind in the vanes of the windmill.

From dawn, and throughout the day, and during the evening and the night, the miller was subjected to incessant reproaches and bitter quarrels because, in the little church, he had gazed for a long time at the blondest of the village girls.

For long months, his life was harsher than that of a captive in the depths of a prison.

Finally, the peevish and jealous wife died; and the miller, whose hair was already going gray, blossomed in felicity. But he hid his joy under the appearances of grief. Everywhere, he praised the merits of his dead wife loudly.

He spoke amorously to the blondest of the village girls, and she replied to him with a smile; and the dream of a happy marriage flourished in the miler's soul.

Now, in the darkness, he heard the large vanes of the windmill turning. Their powerful breath brought him an echo of plaintive sounds.

He recognized the voice of the dead wife.

The dead woman said to him, sadly: "You shivered in horror at the sound of my unfinished complaints; and you feared for a moment that I might surge forth from the tomb where you buried me with feigned tears and false sobs.

"Certainly, I was a peevish wife, with jealousy always alert, but I was also the amorous virgin who paled at the sigh of confessions. I was the white bride who trembled when you ravaged her pure couch, bitterly. Evoke the nocturnal hours when your lips were intoxicated by the savor of my body. Think of the long slumbers in the warmth of our mingled flesh. Relive, O my husband, the nights when I loved you and you loved me."

The miller felt regret for the caresses of old awakening within him. He forgot the torments, the worries and the quarrels, and no longer found anything in his memory but the enchantment of the first amour.

All his being sank into an immense dolor, and fled toward the fjord.

His cadaver floated for a long time on the green waves.

Thus died the village miller.

The dawn of his unaccomplished marriage was resplendent in the serene azure.

The Flowers with no Perfume

A shepherdess was picking flowers on the mountain when the mountain opened up and a hideous black troll surged forth from the depths, blacker than the subterranean night, more hideous than the monsters of the sea.

The troll said to the shepherdess: "Why are you picking flowers on the mountain?"

"They are poor flowers without brightness, which wither in the hand," the shepherdess replied. "They have flowered freely in the air of the summits."

The shepherdess was picking flowers on the mountain.

The troll said to the shepherdess: "Descend with me into the depths. I will give you flowers that never fade, flowers rosier than the roses on the bush, bluer than gentians, whiter than daises. Come and pick eternal flowers with me."

The shepherdess replied: "I would no longer respire the air of the summits. My feet would no longer tread the virgin snow of the peaks. I would no longer see the dusk illuminating the heights."

The troll said to the shepherdess: "Come and weave the eternal flowers with me."

The shepherdess descended into the depths of the mountains.

In a garden of darkness she picked rubies rosier than the roses of the mountain. She picked sapphires bluer than gentians. She picked diamonds whiter than daises. The shepherdess picked the eternal flowers.

But they had no perfume.

Her companions called to her from the height of the rocks.

Her companions shouted to her, weeping.

She held out her arms to them from the depths of the mountain. Her tears flowed over the flowers devoid of perfume; but she could not respond to her companions, for she had already forgotten their language.

She no longer respired the air of the summits; her feet no longer trod the virgin snow; for her eyes were accustomed to the night. She had become blind in the depths of the mountains. She had forgotten the road that led to the summits. She had lost the desire to see the heights again.

The Mute Siren

IN the happy times when the roses of Hellas perfumed the world, the Sirens sang in the night.

They sang the ecstasy of Death, the charm of a voluptuous agony and the coolness of repose beneath the appeased waves.

But suddenly, they fell silent and went pale, for the most beautiful of the Sirens was no longer singing.

She was weeping, and her tears had the glaucous transparency of the waves of the sea. And her immortal sisters asked her, fearfully: "O sweetness of our songs, why do you remain silent in the midst of harmonies?"

She spoke slowly and rhythmically:

"Last night, I saw Psappha of Lesbos die. She came to sob on the Leucadian rock the dolor and the alarm of her last amour. And sometimes, she sang in a strange voice. The sea wind carried her words away.

"I heard her murmur, ardently: 'Atthis, I loved you once . . .' And there was a great silence. Then soft and sonorous names spilled from her lips: 'Gorgo, Anactoria, Dica, Andromeda . . .'

"She evoked tresses and perfumes, reflections and echoes, frissons of fabrics and rays of starlight, smiles and spoken words, the confessions of virgins and the effluvia of roses, all of the incomparable past.

"She intoxicated herself with former sufferings. She savored former sorrows. And, leaning over the sea, she offered her final lamentation to cruel and consoling Aphrodite.

"*Immortal Aphrodite, daughter of Zeus, weaver of ruses, you whose throne hid a thousand colors, I beg you not to break my soul in distress and in anguish, O Sovereign!*

"For, even in her supreme despair, she could not curse the Goddess who had once given her so many bitter felicities.

"She threw herself recklessly into the sea, and I saw the distant pallor of her body carried away by the waves.

"And that is why, O my sisters, I shall no longer sing . . ."

She wept, and her tears had the glaucous transparency of the waves of the sea.

A Tale of the Second of November

AMID the attenuated charm of old furniture, the man who had so avidly and obstinately acquired it was dreaming.

His collection of antique rarities was perhaps unrivaled. And, thinking about the years of studies and searches, he gloried in his long patience and consummate victory.

An old clock chimed slowly and softly, a chime weighed down by the weight of the past. Midnight . . .

A new day was born in the darkness.

In the depths of slumbering rooms, a slight sound quivered, as light as a woman's footfalls, but as sinister as the creaking of the wood of a coffin . . .

And the old collector, suddenly awakened from the idleness by which he was lulled, sensed the horror of the unknown grip him in the night.

The sound grew more emphatic and more profound, and came closer; the shadowed corners filled with mystery, and the silence was populated by visions.

An entire population of phantoms stirred around the petrified old man: strange and disparate specters, of all epochs and all countries.

Finally drawing upon a little courage within his terror, the scholar succeeded in distinguishing forms and faces among the host of shadows. His almost extinct gaze stopped on an old English nobleman whose picturesque costume evoked the times of Queen Anne. His rotund belly caused his blue silk waistcoat dotted with gracious pink flowers to protrude. His nose was ardently lit up in the middle of his congested face. The jovial revenant symbolized peace, order, well-being, good cheer, self-importance and dignity. And his sensual lips were agitating.

"Who are you?" interrogated an echo of a voice, pierced with an inflection of anger. "How dare you usurp the desk on which, laboriously, for long years, I wrote my memoirs, pale memories of a youth of adventures and heroic debauchery?

"You have not even been able to discover the secret drawer, so ingeniously dissimulated, in which the last letter my Beloved sent me is sleeping in an eternal perfume of bitterness and sweetness! For, of all the women who passed through my existence, I only loved one virgin.

"She had eyes the color of sea water, eyes as soft as a reflection; from her corsage, barely open, an odor of hawthorn and foliage emerged; and I never possessed her . . . But how can you know these things, you who disdain embraces and allow the few hours of your existence to pass by amid the peaceful shadow of the Past?"

"What are you, whose placid blood has never burned with the fever of battle, who have never breathed in the red vapor of spilled blood like the fumes of wine, doing with my glorious sword?" complained the profound voice of a Crusader, whose armor was bleached by the starlight. "When I returned, sated with carnage, to my pale chatelaine, whose tenderness was mingled with fear, my caresses had the bitter and voluptuous reek of death . . ."

A Chinaman whose mask was twisted by frightful grimaces and who was uttering incomprehensible words volubly, circled around a battle gong. He seemed to be lamenting no longer being able to hear the prolonged resonance that invited him to massacres . . .

An old Dutch housewife, with an immaculate ruche, like a Rembrandt portrait, sought in vain in a chest of drawers stuffed with delicate and soft linen, in order to touch what she had once arranged there with such meticulous order . . .

A young Florentine youth with the eyes of a perverse girl, a strange ephebe whose body had a feminine suppleness, replaced on his finger the ring whose hollow emerald had once contained a secret and mortal poison . . .

Portuguese pirates fought with dagger thrusts over the booty paid for with their blood . . .

Lords from the court of Louis XIII debated the merits of the thrust of the Cavalier Marin . . .[1]

The erudite old man sensed his reason vacillating, when his wandering eyes were captivated by the delicate and poetic vision of a Marquise. The pallor of powdered hair attenuated the gaiety of her young face. Her impatient lips seemed to be burning under invisible kisses. Her hands were as soft as velvet. Her eyelids were fluttering, and her irises darkening with inexpressible languor.

In her voice, the echo of ancient confessions sang.

"I am saddened," she said, "by the thought that your heavy slumber wallows in that bed garlanded with golden

---

1 The "Cavalier Marin" was the Italian poet Giambatista Marino (1569-1625), who lived in France during the last decade of his life and whose flamboyant style was greatly admired by many of the writers of the French court; his work was still in vogue when the first literary salons came into being.

roses, where I made love so marvelously! What do you know of amour, you who sleep alone? It is on a pillow without repose that I once spread out the odorous snow of my hair. My lips had the perfume of a flower and the flavor of a fruit. The instants of the night went by as ardent and brief as summer lightning, and when I finally went to sleep, burning and weary, it was to dream again of enlacements and embraces . . .

"The appetite for amour consumes me in death, and I have returned, an insatiable lover, in order to seek the shadow of the kisses whose memory torments me in the afterlife. For nothing in infinity is worth an hour of uncertain lust . . ."

A glimmer of twilight interrupted her.

It was the dawn. The gray light grew, came closer, and in confrontation with the daylight that dissipates illusions and brings back verity, the phantoms were dispersed.

The Legend of the Willow

THE FIRST breezes of spring were warming up.
The forests were heavy with the inexhaustible life
of plants and the rut of animals.

Violated Nymphs were fainting of their amorous
wounds, and even the Hamadryads, in their temples of
bark and foliage, were no longer sheltered from the assaults
of Fauns.

Weary of the universal coupling, infinitely weary of
contemplating the brutality of embraces, the youngest of
the Hamadryads had selected as a retreat a tree shedding
almost white and melancholy foliage, the silvery reflections
of which were prolonged over the river.

Thirsty for the limpidity and the innocence of the water,
she leaned avidly toward the moving and sonorous brightness of the surface; and she implored the Divinities of the
river to grant her the coolness of repose and forgetfulness
of caresses.

As she leaned over, she thought she perceived pale
blonde hair floating on the surface of the water with the
fluidity of algae. And, drawing closer to that moist gleam,
she thought she saw eyes of a blue as subtle as the blue of
the waves: a gaze as mobile and fleeting as the flux and
reflux of the river itself.

Divinely and terrible dazzled, she saw the Naiad smiling at her with a smile that seemed attractive and promising, and she had the presentiment of mortal amours . . .

Returned to consciousness of herself, she sought again, but in vain, for the mysterious illusion of that visage.

The dream had disappeared.

Only a ripple in the water marked the place where the limpid undulating smile had trembled.

She leaned over further, ever more smitten with the shadow of the Naiad, the dream of fugitive beauty and uncertain amour.

Her hair, of a silvery green, dipped into the river, and mingled with the reeds and white irises.

A frisson of fear and desire caused her long, flexible and frail body to shiver all the way to the roots of her being.

She waited.

On a moonlit winter night, she thought she had found the pale hair again, luminously spread out, but it was only the scintillation of starlight quivering on the water.

Then she despaired.

The nenuphars, those strange lilies of lakes and rivers, sprung from the slumber of the water, chaste and cold like her, seemed to be the drowned faces of amorous virgins who had once sought forgetfulness in the depths of the river bed.

The white irises had melancholy for the forsaken. Everything was weeping with sadness and abandonment.

In a surge of passion and prayer, the Hamadryad launched one last appeal toward the nocturnal eddies.

"O Form born from the ripples of the water, you who incarnate in your undulating body all the graces of the river, O Beauty who slips between the arms, who flees embraces, who escapes kisses, will you never come back to overwhelm me and delight me with your half-revealed charm?"

No breath stirred the summit of the waves, and the Hamadryad of the Willow understood that the expectation of amour is as vain as the smile of the water that enabled her to glimpse the perfidious image of a Naiad.

But, possessed by the immortal life of all Divinities of imperishable Hellas, she cannot forget her dolor. She is the Afflicted; she is inconsolable, and weeps her long green tears eternally into rivers.

The Impossible Perfection

A man anxious to develop his soul to the point of perfection meditated upon the words of the Saints and the Prophets for a long time.

Christ, he thought, *was not the perfect Being. He poured forgiveness on abominations committed, but the abysm of sin was unknown to him. That God who was made man was ignorant of half of human joys and dolors. He was a stranger to the dazzle of desire and the magnificent anguish of remorse. The man who has not sinned is not the perfect Being.*

And the man who aspired to the absolute beauty of his soul decided to know all the defects and all the lusts that damn and save humans.

He wanted to know the charm of murder.

And, knowing that modern life only offers poor soil in which the bloody flower of crime is etiolating, he fled toward ardent and free spaces.

Amid the gold of overturned cups and the breath of roses, he ordered the burning of naked women.

He invented refined tortures in which amour espoused death.

Before crucifying them, he intoxicated the passivity of ephebes and the pollution of children.

One evening, he incarnated Heliogabalus; one night, he resuscitated Nero.

Then, weary, he returned to incomplete civilization. He was the Gambler whose triumphal march sowed thousands of ruinations.

Around his dwelling, faces of hunger and despair grimaced.

He had heard the appeals of the distressed and the gasps of suicides.

In the crimson of a summer dusk, he raped his sister; and he murdered his father secretly.

He was the anonymous thief who robbed passers-by in the mystery of the streets and the shadows of highways.

He was the vulgar assassin who goes to sleep on the tender heart of a prostitute.

He knew all disgusts, all shames, all cowardices and all glories.

Then, recovering the broad peace of the autumnal countryside, he thought about repentance. He remembered his superhuman aspirations of old.

Before the insignificance of his crimes, the mediocrity of the most enormous sins, he was unable to savor the somber and mystical splendor of Repentance.

He dreamed of a magnanimous death that would leave in the depths of the human heart an eternal reflection of horror and pity; but a banal fever came one day to surprise him in his bed. Thus died the man who had only lacked a little in order to become the perfect Being.

The Profane Genesis

I. BEFORE the birth of the Universe two eternal principles existed, Jehovah and Satan.

II. Jehovah incarnated might, Satan cunning.

III. Now, the two great principles hated one another with a profound hatred.

IV. In those times, Chaos reigned.

V. Jehovah said: "Let there be light." And there was light.

VI. And Satan created the mystery of the night.

VII. Jehovah breathed over the immensity, and his breath gave birth to the Heavens.

VIII. Satan covered the implacable azure with the fleeting grace of clouds.

IX. From the laborious hands of Jehovah came the spring.

X. Satan dreamed the melancholy of autumn.

XI. Jehovah conceived the robust or svelte forms of animals.

XII. Under the furtive smile of Satan, flowers sprang forth.

XIII. Jehovah kneaded clay; and from that clay, he made man.

XIC. From the very essence of that flesh flourished, idealized, the flesh of Woman, the work of Satan.

XV. Jehovah curbed man and woman under violence and the embrace.

XVI. Satan taught them the sharp subtlety of the caress.

XVII. Jehovah formed with the breath the soul of a Poet.

XVIII. He inspired the Aede of Ionia, the powerful Homer.

XIX. Homer celebrated the magnificence of carnage and the glory of bloodshed, the ruination of cities, the sobs of widows, devastating flames, the flash of swords and the shock of battles.

XX. Satan inclined, toward the west, over the repose of the Lesbian Psappha.

XXI. And she sang the fugitive forms of amour; the pallors and the ecstasies; the magnificent unfurling of tresses; the burning perfume of roses; the rainbow, the throne of Aphrodite; the bitterness and sweetness of Eros; the sacred dances of the women of Crete around the starlit altar; the solitary slumber into which, in the night of the moon and the Pleiades, the immortal pride sinks which scorns dolor and smiles in death; and the charm of feminine kisses rhythmed by the muffled flux of the sea expiring under the voluptuous walls of Mytilene.

FROM GREEN TO VIOLET

Lilith
(A Hebrew Legend)

Fundamentally, believe me,
woman has only ever loved the serpent.
(Villiers de l'Isle Adam[1])

L ILITH was created before Eve.
       She was more beautiful than the Mother of the human race. She was not drawn from the flesh of the man but born from a breath of the dawn.

Her crimson hair set the dusk ablaze and her eyes reflected the beauty of the universe.

When he created Lilith, God destined her to smile at the man. But she considered the man and found him coarse in essence and inferior to herself.

And she turned her eyes away from Adam.

One evening, while she was wandering in the triumphal gardens of Eden, she saw the ineffably dolorous gaze of Satan posed upon her.

He had put on the undulating and supple form of the Serpent, and his eyes were sparkling like pale emeralds.

He said to the woman: "You do not know the mystery of Amour.

---

1 The quotation is from the drama *Morgane* (1866).

45

"You are wrong to scorn your disgraceful companion, for you can teach him and learn from him unknown joys."

Lilith contemplated the strange eyes, like two pale emeralds.

And she replied to him: "You're lying, and you're tempting me with the vulgar bait of pleasures devoid of beauty.

"You also know the secrets of subtle sensuality that resemble the Infinite.

"You, who are tempting me with amorous words, be my mystical lover.

"I shall not conceive and I shall not give birth under the ardor of your embrace.

"But our dreams will populate the earth, and our chimeras will be incarnate in the Future."

There was a vibrant silence between them.

And from the intercourse of Lilith and the Serpent were born the perverse dreams, the maleficent perfumes and the poisons of revolt and lust that haunt the human spirit and render the human soul similar to the sad and dangerous soul of Angels of Evil.

The Dogaressa

THE DOGARESSA is weeping in the depths of the Palace.

She is jealous, she is neglected and she is lamenting in solitude.

For this is the dawn of the sacred day when the Doge must espouse the Sea.

The salt of kisses, like the salt of tears, floats in the air.

And the sea is adorned with light; the Sea has put on her nuptial robe, her robe of sunlight.

The Dogaressa is weeping in the depths of the Palace.

For the Dogaressa is jealous of the Sea, the eternal Lover who steals her husband from her.

"You whose eyes have the melancholy of lagoons, you whose eyes retain the reflection of dead waters, O pitiful and jealous Dogaressa, listen to me.

"I know the secrets of the sea.

"She is ardent and sterile, she loves the amour of the Moon and scorns the amour of men.

"She awaits with anxiety the hour of darkness, which will unite her with her mystical Lover.

"When their kisses mingle, you will see a shudder and hear the plaint of your Rival.

"The Moon and the Sea will love one another tonight, in the profundity of space.

"Have no fear, O Dogaressa; at dusk, the Sea will return your husband to you.

"You will find him pale with unslaked desire, and you will press his bitter lips with yours for a long time.

"But do not be frightened if your husband no longer returns your caresses, for those whom the Sea has disdained die of her scorn.

"Tonight, the Moon and the Sea will love one another in the profundity of space."

The Heroic Tomb

I saw a tomb without flowers in a cemetery where all the flowers of regret and memory were blooming: roses as pale as suffering, pansies as somber as remorse, and violets as sad as dreams.

A man who was passing spat on the tomb without flowers and when I criticized the sacrilegious act with a gesture, he said to me: "I am condemning the tomb of a coward."

I meditated until dusk, respiring the flowers of regret and memory, and the Sunset glorified the tomb with a tragic aureole.

Under the shadow of the cypresses, a motionless and white form that I had not noticed among the marble statues became animated and came toward me, slowly and resolutely.

"The passer-by lied," she said. "This tomb consecrates a heroic memory. You can read on the marble the name of a man who died voluntarily. He overcame the most powerful instinct, that of Life. He triumphed over nature, in her greatest tenacity, by means of the Act of Destruction. And that is why I have traced in letters of gold on the funeral monument the words that my tears have not been able to efface:

"*He has vanquished.*"

"No," I replied, "he has done better still; he has liberated himself."

"Is that not the greatest victory?" she asked me.

. . . And the dusk drank our words.

49

A Woman's Hair

I love a woman's hair with an amour in which a little fear is mingled; for it possesses a separate existence, a strange and almost terrible existence. I have known women of a disquieting fragility whose excessive hair had exhausted all their strength, and who died of the weight of their hair. And the tresses of dead women have been seen still alive and extending in the depths of the tomb . . .

A princess of legend once expired in the pale flower of her virginity. Her father, the king, had that divine intact body, which resembled the petrified reflection of pearls and the perfume of white roses, buried in a tomb of black marble. She slept therein for a hundred years. But a poet-king put on the crown and, after having collected ancient ballads that glorified the undulating tresses of the princess of legend, he had the black marble tomb opened, in order to discover a supreme vestige of all that beauty, the memory of which still sang on the lips of humans.

Having penetrated into the mausoleum, he recoiled, terrified and delighted; for the tresses of the dead princess were streaming like marvelous moonlight and illuminating the sepulchral darkness with their glimmers of crystal and silver. Their cold blondes were composed of all the blues of the evening, all the greens of the night, and all the unreal gold of the stars. And the hair enveloped the mesh of a skeleton as fine as the tenuous threads of a spider-web extended over dew . . .

Through the ages, the immortal hair had survived the virgin whose pride and joy it had been.

A Dorian Tale

I taught Hero of Guara, the fleet virginal runner.
(Psappha)

LIKE Atalanta, Hero of Guara was a virgin, fleet in running. The crowd contemplated from afar her flying golden sandals, as prompt as lightning, when she was the first to reach the finish, the morning breeze having loosened her hair and heightened the aurora of her cheeks. Breaths of fennel and thyme impregnated her body and floated around her.

She had the vast and empty soul of solitudes. Her dream was as imprecise as space, and the desire for amour had never enfevered the freshness of her eyes, in which a reflection of grass and foliage quivered.

One evening, she was listening to the murmur of the sea, eternally smitten with Mytilene, the sea that tightens her profound embrace around the sacred isle, when she heard a voice singing, as amorous as the sea:

"Come, goddess of Kupros, and pour nectar mingled with joys into golden cups."

And slowly, a woman emerged from the meditative shadow of trees and stopped in front of the stranger, saying: "I am Psappha of Lesbos."

Her hair was interlaced with hyacinths, her hair of nocturnal profundities, undulating in the breeze, and her eyes, as blue as the Aegean, unfathomable and changing, attracted like very deep water. She had the pallor of grass that the sun has discolored. Her hands were perfumed with violets, of which she wove crowns. Her voice was similar to the voice of Peitho, the persuasion that serves Aphrodite and which draws beings toward amour. And her smile had the distant softness of the smile of Selanna.[1]

Hero contemplated her, mutely. The ardent redness of the evening burned their faces. A silence full of tremors enveloped them both.

Their dissimilar beauty harmonized and was completed, and their dreams of sensuality were united.

"Come," said the Lesbian, finally. "I will teach you songs and amour."

She approached, and the lips of the virgin agonized beneath the flame of the kiss.

---

1 Just as Vivien preferred the Dorian rendering of Psappha [Sappho], so she preferred Kupros to Cyprus or Kypris (the goddess in question being Aphrodite) and Selanna to Selene.

The Unknown Divinity

THE woman I love, the unknown woman, dwells in the depths of an antique palace in which a perpetual dusk is obstinate.

The old Venetian palace where her childhood germinated, where her adolescence flourished, slumbers in the silence of dead waters. The shadow of the past blurs the fragile nuances of fabrics and the colors of paintings. One can scarcely hear the sea breezes quivering in the pleats of the heavy curtains. There is silence within her and around her.

One divines, on approaching her, that she has always lived in solitude. She has long hands, to which the penumbra has given the yellow tones of old ivory. Her gaze has the reflection of dead waters. She speaks in such a low voice that one has to concentrate in order to hear her. And her speech resembles the echo of a plaint that no one has ever heard.

In the chamber that she inhabits, one senses the mysterious presence of the Soul. She loves the flowers that fade and is voluptuously saddened when dusk causes the petals of a rose to fall.

Her mourning dress has the soft thickness of darkness. It is as if she were enveloped by the night.

Her hair is woven of nocturnal radiance and mingled with purple, as if the Shadow were shredding calm violets there.

I love her because she is unknown to me and only exists in a dream.

54

Fishhooks

A Scot, a childhood friend, showed me his collection of fishhooks one day.

"Look," he said to me, "this is a veritable museum. These fishhooks that you see are works of art. To attract salmon, which nourish themselves on iridescent flies in flight, we have invented light fishhooks, golden, green, blue and violet. Some are fashioned with the feathers of pheasants, and you know that the pheasant has all the magnificence of the peacock, augmented with the inexpressible grace of savage beings. These fishhooks demand patient labor and expert ingenuity."

I looked at those strange jewels of torture and death. They were, in fact, quite beautiful, as brilliant as glory, and as sparkling as amour.

"And," my interlocutor went on, "the salmon, which believes that it is catching the rainbow and opal wings of errant flies, feels its throat implacably rent by the steel hook; it struggles in vain; it is prey to the Enemy."

As I leaned over the jewels of torture and death, my friend the Scot asked: "What do you think of my collection?"

"I think," I replied to him, "that the Bible—from which I have heard you draw such copious citations—has not lied, and that God has veritably created men in his own image."

Translation of a Polish Song (1)

I hate the woman I love, and I love the woman I hate.

I would like to torture expertly the bruised limbs of the woman I love.

I would like to drink her sighs and her dolor and the plaints of her agony.

I would like to stifle slowly the breath of her breast.

I would like an implacable dagger to bite her all the way to her heart.

And I would rejoice to see all the blood from her veins weeping, drop by drop.

I would cherish her death on the bed of our caresses.

I love the woman I hate.

When I glimpse her in a crowd, I sense, burning within me, the incurable desire to embrace her in front of everyone and possess her in the light.

The rancorous words change on my lips into sobs of desire.

I drive her away with all my anger and I appeal to her with all my sensuality.

She is ferocious and cowardly, but her body is ardent and fresh—a flame melted in dew . . .

I cannot see her perfidious glances and her lying lips without disturbance and without regret . . .

I hate the woman I love, and I love the woman I hate.

The Rocking Chair

"I am astonished," I say to my silent and understanding listeners, "that people strive to discover the secret of perpetual motion. Human beings would be wiser if they employed their noisy ingenuity for preference in discovering the secret of immutable repose."

The old furniture to which I was addressing myself approved with a cordial silence. Only an American rocking chair protested, in a prolonged shudder.

I thought I ought to appease it with conciliatory words.

"I'm not an irreducible adversary of progress," I affirmed. "Comfort attracts me, even under the least seductive external appearance. Comfort is the friend and the protector of dreaming. It shelters it against the inconveniences that trouble thought; and matter, by way of a glorious revenge, aids the highest flight of spirituality. Thus, the even sway of this rocking chair provides a familiar rhythm for the dream. It seems to me that I can hear the monotonous cadence of oars and feel the rocking of the boat that is carrying me away into the distance."

While expressing my approval of modern wisdom I adapted my meditations to the methodical rhythm of the rocking chair. At length, however, my impatient mind demanded beneficent immobility, the immobility once hatched in the languor of an Oriental evening. I coveted the profound peace that an ancestral armchair offered me, and I made an effort to get up.

All my liberating efforts were in vain. Sometimes as stormy as a boat tossed by the waves, and sometimes as regular as the oscillation of a cradle, the rocking chair carried me away in a ceaseless frenzy . . .

I had, without wanting to—oh, certainly, without wanting to—discovered the secret of perpetual motion.

The Iconoclast

I saw a man entering proudly the shadow of the Temple, where the ancient icons reigned in silence.

They were the emblem of all human ferocities; they symbolized the implacable hatred of man for the crime from which he does not profit and the cowardice of the human spirit before the Presence of Death. They were grimacing with all the ancient terrors, their stone eyes containing the gaze of all injustices and all severities. A few raised a hand in a gesture of hypocritical benediction.

The man contemplated them without a word, and his eyes were radiant with a sacred fury. He advanced, and, as irresistible as destiny, he broke the fragile icons. Then, snatching a torch from the altar, he burned the Temple, and the Temple collapsed, and was no longer anything but an accumulation of stones and ash.

The iconoclast stood, triumphant, amid the smoking rubble.

I said to him in an indecisive voice: "O Destroyer of ancient Idols, was your action wise? What will happen tomorrow, when the crowd, having come to offer its adorations and prayers, no longer finds anything but an altar buried beneath a temple in ruins?

"The crowd, liberated from the effects of old, and too blind to raise itself to a superior conception of the worlds and beings, will deliver itself to abominable debaucheries and imbecilic cruelties on the very spot where pious clouds of incense rose.

"What have you done, O Destroyer, and do you not fear the Dawn that seems to be breaking in the uncertainty of the sky?"

The iconoclast looked at me with a serene pride, and replied to me, still illuminated by this victory:

"What does it matter? The superb instant in which man annihilates a false divinity is worth more than the patient labor that gives birth to a memorable work.

"When the crowd invades the abandoned sanctuary tomorrow, and soils it with ignoble gestures and infamous words, I shall destroy myself, in order that the Dream might be consummated."

Popular Song

"O laborer already stooped, not by age but by toil and misery, why are you sowing the wheat?"

"I'm sowing the wheat for the joy of others."

"O mason, why are you building the splendid walls of that dwelling?"

"I'm building these walls for the joy of others."

"O miner, why are you searching for stones and gold in the nocturnal depths of the earth?"

"I'm searching for emeralds, rubies, opals and gold for the joy of others."

"O musician, why are you evoking the storm and the alternate sweetness of sounds?"

"I'm evoking music for the joy of others."

"O prostitute, why have you ornamented your expertly-arranged hair with flowers? Why have you masked your pallor with make-up? Why that profusion of perfumes that emanates from your weary flesh? Why that laughter on your bitter lips?"

"I have put up my hair, covered my pallor, perfumed my body and dissimulated my rancor for the joy of others."

The Glacier
(A Swiss Song)

THE glacier is as blue as the flame of sulfur and as green as aquamarine.

The glacier has the profundity and the majesty of a motionless sea.

The air around the glacier is as cold and pure as crystal.

But dread, O passer-by, the mystery of that water devoid of ripples, for the cold burns with more intensity than fire itself.

In the depths of her palace, as blue as the flame of sulfur and as green as aquamarine, the Virgin of the Glaciers awaits the victims of her splendor.

Those who have loved her have died of her gaze.

I once saw the green and blue eyes of the Virgin of the Glaciers.

She enticed me, from the depths of the abyss, and I would have given all the uncertain sensualities of existence for the bite of her cruel kiss.

The ardor of very cold things consumed me, the intoxication of chastity enchanted me . . .

I once saw the green and blue eyes of the Virgin of the Glaciers.

The Idea Store

IN an old quarter of the city I perceived a strange little shop to which no display and no sign attracted the gaze, and in which no merchant was on the lookout for strollers.

I went in. A man, of whom I could only see the silhouette, so impenetrable was the shadow around us, appeared noiselessly.

"What can you possibly sell here?" I asked him, in the irreflection of my surprise.

"Ideas," he replied to me, in a very simple tone.

He picked up a casket and, seemingly stirring the dust:

"Are you a utopian, by any chance? Pardon my indiscretion. Would you like ideas of peace and universal happiness? They aren't dear and I'm selling a great many of them at present. Look, here's a whole batch for two francs fifty."

And, following my gesture of refusal:

"Oh, you're right; I can't guarantee their solidity. Now, here's a financier's idea, but it's extremely rare and costly. I can't let you have it for less than three thousand francs."

"Damn!" I said. "Three thousand francs is . . ."

He interrupted me calmly.

"An idea less new than that one made the fortune of a founder of American trusts. I don't profit from it personally, because being rich would be too tedious. I'd lose my friends and the consideration of the quarter."

Something like a glint of gold shone between his fingers.

"Now, if, like me, you scorn opulence, or if, which is more probable, the price of that idea seems too high, here, very cheap, is a poet's dream. Three sous—that's reasonable, don't you think?"

He showed me a rainbow glimmer imprisoned in a paint-box.

"Finally, as you appear to me to belong to the serious clientele. I propose to you"—his face creased into a grimace that might have been a smile—"a magnificent libertine idea, entirely unpublished, you know, and of an exceptional refinement. I'll let you have it for a thousand francs. It's worth more, but it's in order for you to come back often and buy others from me. I have a veritably unparalleled collection of them."

"Yes," I said, "but some of your merchandise appears to be very worn."

"Ah!" he replied, with pride. "Those, like antique furniture, are justly the most appreciated by my clientele. But don't you see anything that can satisfy you?"

"I desire an idea that you could never sell me: an idea of my own."

The Forest

COME into the forest, come into the fraternal darkness. Come, I shall collect for you the flowers that resemble you, the nocturnal flowers that harbor subtle poisons.

I shall ornament your lunar tresses with aconite, foxglove and belladonna . . .

Are you not frightened to be alone with me, in the nocturnal forest that loves me and which hates you?

I should like to flee from your bright eyes, as penetrating as mortal steel; I should like to flee from you and draw you to me.

The branches of the trees incline toward you like long menacing arms that stifle in an embrace of hateful amour.

They might strangle you, but they are impotent against me, because I am the being of silence and solitude.

The entire nocturnal forest menaces you and hates you; it has seen the lie in your eyes, and the peril of your voice, and the cruelty of your caress.

But I love you, while wanting to flee from you, and I will protect you against the forest and against myself.

Tender and true things are begging me to abandon you and flee—the foliage and the ivy, and the moss and the beloved violets.

Only the fervent serpents and the moon rejoice and encourage our amour.

Oh, how sinister the voice of the owls is!

The owls are advising me to abandon you and to flee.

The bats with blue wings go astray, tormented by the weight of their bodies and the impotence of their wings.

Their soul is similar to my soul. They collide with one another stupidly, and the desire for infinity is in their blind eyes.

I feel, cruelly, the desire to soar . . .

If I could fly, I might perhaps be able to escape you, O incarnation of my desire.

And if I dared to love you, I would kill you, in accordance with the desire of the nocturnal forest, which would bury you under the foliage and under the branches.

I would stifle your last gasp with my kisses . . . Oh, your last gasp in the night! I would stifle you with embraces and caresses, and you would die of my lips . . .

For I am the Lover who cannot love without hate, and whose covetousness is made of bitterness and melancholy.

And you, you are the Evil Mistress who exasperates fevers and intensifies the malady.

Do you not sense the danger around you?

The odor of Death is in the air and is intoxicating me strangely . . .

Oh, how sinister the voice of the owls is!

"The Moon is laughing, the Moon is laughing . . ."

A Porcelain Poem

SHE had the fragile smile and delicate coloration of the little Dresden shepherdess who plays mute music eternally in my display case.

I loved her, that charmingly frail child, during an entire autumn. I still love her, with a melancholy tenderness, like the compassionate breath that rises gently from dead leaves.

Oh, the refined, slightly precious, poetry of her slight gestures. One evening, she strewed rose petals on the threshold of our chamber of amour.

I remember one moonless winter night, a starry night clearer than crystal and dew. The trees, florid with frost, were very pale and similar to silver sculptures. Foliage no longer weighed down the thin design of the branches. Everything was white, everything was radiant with a vague light.

The shadows were transparent, and I could see in the dark.

I wanted to wake up the virgin with the frail charm and reveal to her the pure miracle of the sky and the earth, but I hesitated before the mystery of slumber. Something solemn emanated from that motionless body and those closed eyelids. She seemed as sacred to me as a corpse languishing beneath flowers.

When she ceased to love me, when she knew the pollution of marriage, there was a slight and persistent dolor within me . . . that dolor that one experiences in seeing a rare porcelain statuette broken.

An Irish Tale

DANA, the Creatrice of Things, the immemorial and omnipotent Mother of the universe, resolved to chastise the beings who were stupidly violating the law of mildness, liberty, frankness and love.

And omnipotent Dana said to the Night: "O my most beautiful work, flowered between my laborious hands, withdraw from the earth."

There was then the horror of the eternal Day. Owls opened their large wounded eyes fearfully, their eyes in which glimmers of gold lit up in the depths of darkness. Bats, maddened by the universal radiation, clashed their dolorous wings without respite. The nocturnal flowers died without delivering their subtle perfumes to the violet air, and women moaned, their bruised eyelids no longer knowing the consolation of shadow.

And the Night implored Dana the Creatrice: "O Dana, see how the Sea is lamenting, for her waves are no longer caressed by the Moon. See how the solitudes are saddened, for their mystery is no more, and they are frightened in seeing themselves revealed in the light."

Appeased, Dana listened to the voice of the Night kneeling at her feet, under her innumerable veils, green and purple and russet and blue. And omnipotent Dana rendered the Night to the earth.

The Lovers of Death

DEATH appeared to me one winter evening. Her robe seemed woven of moonlight, snow and tears. Death said to me: "Follow me into my palace, whose marble shines in the midst of cypresses. There I will show you the multitude of my lovers. They are brighter and more majestic than living Beauty, and no human intoxication can equal the ardor of the embrace with which they once enlaced me."

I took the road to the tombs and I saw the multitude of the lovers of Death.

Some had known the coolness of her lips on the fluid bed of rivers and seas. Others had sought her in the anguish of poison or the cruel flash of steel. All of them retained on their brow the reflection of a decisive thought and a solemn act.

I saw the multitude of the lovers of Death, those who had dared to accomplish the most magnificent human gesture: self-destruction. And I envied the peace and splendor that radiated from their faces.

I asked them whether, in truth, the kiss of Death was clement and sweet.

And their response was the plenitude of silence.

To the Perverse Ophelia

I once carried you to the water you love, the water that resembles you, and I drowned you . . .

And the water has become a stagnant marsh.

Like a perverse Ophelia, you float on the surface of the livid pool.

Your blossoming breasts are two nenuphars, and your glaucous blonde hair is entangled like fluvial algae.

Your brow is as green as the water, your gaze as motionless and blue as the stagnant water.

You repose among the reeds and the irises, since the day when, with my amorous hands, with my criminal hands, I drowned you . . .

The Eternal Slave

I saw Woman charged with chains of gold and chains of bronze. Her bonds were both as tenuous as a cobweb and as heavy as the mass of mountains, and Man, sometimes a torturer and sometimes a parasite, dominated and lived off her.

Docile, she submitted to the tyranny. And her greatest fear was hearing the hypocritical words of amour that were mingled with the master's orders.

I cried to Woman—and my cry traversed the grilles that separated us, desperately:

"O You, the eternal Afflicted, disappointed Tenderness, Martyr of amour, why resign yourself with a degrading patience to the ignominy and cowardice of that false companion? Are you submitting out of amour or out of dread?"

She replied to me: "I am submitting neither out of amour nor out of dread, but by virtue of ignorance and habitude."

And those words brought me an immense sadness and an immense hope.

Viviane

IN the forest of Broceliande, I recognized Viviane.

She seemed to be made of shadow, and her gaze was as blue as the crepuscular foliage.

"Muffle your footsteps, which are making the dead leaves crackle," she said, "for there is no cruelty more hateful than that of waking a sleeping individual. The visages of those who are asleep resemble, in their beatitude, the visages of those whom Death has laid on a bed of violets. To wake a sleeping individual is to bring him, once again, worries, anguish, memories, remorse and all the melancholy of living. So do not wake Merwynn, who is asleep amid the primroses and wild lilies."

I contemplated her with the delighted eyes of my soul and I sobbed:

"O Viviane, the caresses of other women only provide sensuality; yours provide forgetfulness. Can you not grant me, who loves you, the lightning of a kiss?"

"I do not love the shadows who pass by," she replied. "Merwynn alone possesses my incomparable amour."

"And yet," I said, "you betrayed him, Viviane."

"Yes, I betrayed him," murmured the witch of Broceliande. "But is it not the destiny of humans eternally to betray those they love? Whether the treason is mediocre or immense, it slips irremediably through the lips that possess. Yes, I betrayed Merwynn. I dispossessed him of wisdom, but I have given him what is infinitely more precious: the annihilation of thought."

The Song of the One Who Passes By

"To what harmony will you deign to listen this evening, O Silent One? Would you like the harmony of the nightingale? Would you like the savant complexity of chords or the unique sob of song?"

"I only want to hear the moaning of the Scorn of the Moon."

"With what flowers would you like to adorn your nocturnal tresses, in which the russet and the blue are in harmony? Would you like delicately artificial gardenia that a touch bruises? Would you like the ardent rose or the lily, even more voluptuous in her amorous pallor and the vehemence of her breath? Would you like the cyclamen with the tender fragrance or the black iris, or the poppy that emits an odor of slumber?"

"I only want tenebrous violets, sisters of the Night."

"With what clarities would you like to illuminate the banqueting hall? Would you like the red flame of torches or the mystical radiance of candles whose odorous wax dissolves into perfumes? Would you like the inexpressible light of the nebulous stars?"

"I only want the large eyes of owls, which are gilded in the darkness."

"What Beauty would you like to contemplate with your ardent eyes? Would you like the subtle blondes of tresses blurred by green and pink reflections? Would you like the autumnal magnificence of red hair or the profundity of black hair? Would you like the infinity of blue eyes, the flame of dark eyes, the twilight of gray eyes, or the enigma of green eyes?"

"I only want to contemplate the visage of Solitude, my Lover and my Friend."

Death's Rainbow

I
Green

HER body stole away with vague undulations, and the limpid syllables of her name streamed over her lips.

She had gone to the river's edge and she had detached a boat, because she wanted to drift on the pale green water, the water that resembled her and which she loved.

She drifted on the water; the willows allowed their long, loose tresses to dangle; the meadows sparkled like bight emeralds, and the eyes of the little friend of the water were puerile with the candor of Greens.

Suddenly, she leaned over to pluck nenuphars, as white as the surf of the northern seas, as pink as the moon and as blue as morning mists, which were dreaming on the surface of the water and spreading languor and sleep around them. And she leaned over, she leaned over . . .

And the empty boat drifted downstream, while the virgin with the green flesh struggled desperately . . .

For the terrible fluvial algae gripped her with their long arms, like the arms of cephalopods, and drew her irresistibly and fatally toward them . . .

Thus died the little friend of the Water, a cool and green death, and the water wept for a long time and buried her under reeds and black irises . . .

And in memory of her, the waves caused to blossom, in the place where she had disappeared, nenuphars as white as the surf of northern seas, as pink as the moon, and as blue as morning mists . . .

II
Orange

The setting sun had the velvet of a beautiful ripe fruit, the air was heavily laden with the sensual perfume of orchards, and the Lover sated herself on the breast of her Lover.

She had wanted to die in the supreme expansion of the Kiss, and now the moment had come, the moment was as velvety as a beautiful ripe fruit, weighed down by the sensual perfume that rose from orchards.

She sought her Lover's lips, the lips with the amber down, and knew reciprocal voluptuousness for the last time.

And she died a carnally orange death in the plenitude of the sunset.

III
Violet

Kathleen came from magical Ireland, where the harmony of the Green reigns in all its freshness, where the marshes are haunted by strange errant flames like the gleams of souls, which the Fays have chosen as their supreme refuge, and where the women have moist violet eyes.

Kathleen trailed the burden of her youth out there in magical Ireland.

She was weary of having supported the springs and their unrealizable hopes, the summers and their unslaked ardor, the autumns and their limitless sadness, the winters and their chaste severity.

She had tasted the bitterness of betraying the woman she loved the most, of abandoning her dreams, of seeing herself inferior to her destiny. She had learned to know herself, to detest the baseness of her heart and the cowardice of her soul. And, having looked Life in the face, she judged it as vain as it was hateful.

She died of her own will on a purple night, a vast, calm night. The clouds were as fluid as algae in a sea devoid of eddies.

And she lay down on a bed of violets, and died a perfumed death, a slow and gentle death that consoled her for having lived.

The Apparition

I saw a woman advancing toward me, as ardent and pure as the snow. Her dress had amorous creases; the vehement effluvia of lilies floated around her. The sadness and sensuality of the sea emanated from her, and also the radiance of death.

She said: "To the soul that I love, I teach the hatred of spring and the amour of autumn. I am the sister of long ago and of sleep. I bring in my hands the perfumes of Solitude. I am the woman who knows neither regret nor remorse."

I invoked her piously: "You who shine with such a resplendent pallor, do you not bring a balm for inexpressible human suffering?"

Oh, the smile on her lips, which had not pronounced the word *irreparable*!

"I do not cure suffering, I suppress it," she replied, very slowly. "Through me, and through me alone, *dolor is not*. I am Sterility."

The Song of the Sirens

I

"I should like," said Ione with the violet eyes, lingering on the crepuscular shore, "to hear the Song of the Sirens."

"You know very well," replied the old fisherman Meniskos, "that the Song of the Sirens is mortal to those who hear it."

"Like everything that is beautiful and sonorous," the virgin with the violet eyes interjected, imperiously. "Only things without grandeur contain no danger."

"The sage Ulysses gave his companions the advice to block their ears with wax and attach themselves to the masts of the vessel," added Meniskos.

"Ulysses was nothing but a coward," cried the very young and very imperious Ione. "And his companions were also nothing but cowards. Prudence is eternal cowardice. Oh, to prefer the tedious Penelope to the Sirens! Myself, I would give the breath of my lips, the line, undulations and colors that my avid eyes contemplate with so much anguish, the harmonies that make me suffer so divinely, the perfumes that I respire with so much fever, everything that makes life burning and sad, to hear the Song of the Sirens for an instant . . . And the kisses of my companions, the kisses that are like harmonies, perfumes, the joy of colors, lines and graceful undulations, the kisses as bitter as the sky and as sweet as roses, I would give them all to hear the perilous Song for an instant."

"In truth, your words are not wise," said old Meniskos, calmly. "What! You would give the long years of a human existence for a lightning flash of joy?"

"You cannot understand, Meniskos," Ione replied. "Men are cowards from birth. Only two instincts make them act: pride and bestiality. No man would ever give his existence to hear the Song of the Sirens."

Meniskos shrugged his shoulders, and went away, toward the hearth and the evening meal. In the twilight, Ione detached the boat, which was lost in the mist in which Visions floated.

She wandered for three days and three nights. And the Sirens appeared to her, in a green moonlight that broke over the waves . . .

Their song was as imprecise as the song of the waves; it attracted like the mysterious appeal of the waves; it unfurled with a grave amplitude, like the sob of the Ocean; it gripped the soul of Ione, who sank voluptuously into the waves . . .

II

She awoke, the drowned child with the violet eyes, under the fluid kisses of a Siren whose hair enveloped her like networks of algae. She awoke under the ungraspable gaze of green eyes, which had the perfidious softness of the waves. She awoke under the troubled smile of the Siren, whose voice, like the distant sound of waves on crepuscular shores, said to her:

"Since you have loved us resolutely enough to give us your human existence, we will give you in our turn the fervor of our kiss. See, I have collected with my own hands, in order to ornament your hair, the pearls that are the pale flowers of the Sea, and multicolored nacre, and the infinite grace of marvelous seashells. Your repose on the velvet of the silver sand will be lulled by the rhythm of the Sea. You will play with the crabs and you will smile at the medusae that burn like the stars. In the gardens of the Sea, living anemones are blue, and in her orchards, trees of coral sway their red branches at the whim of the eddies. You will hear the Sea's song of eternally unappeased amour, the song that rises toward the Moon, her distant Lover. For Death cures all memories, and Death is very beautiful on the bed of the Sea."

To Living Death

I bring strange flowers to your memory, O living Death, who exists and does not exist, who rejoices and sobs outside our amour.

I bring you blue orchids, the subtle and pale blue of your eyes, winter roses of a green whiteness similar to the whiteness of your flesh, and gardenias bruised by the slightest contact, gardenias similar to the morbidity of your artificial soul, which everything wounds, irritates and ruffles . . .

I bring strange flowers to your memory, O living Death, who exists and does not exist, who rejoices and sobs outside our amour . . .

The Interrogation

A woman enveloped in long violet garments with nocturnal reflections was wandering, knocking on all doors. Some opened, and, of the inhabitants of those dwellings, she asked, in the voice with which one begs for alms:

"Tell me who I am, what I am, and why I am."

And the inhabitants went back into their houses, the threshold of which Fear had not yet crossed. None pronounced to the interrogator the vain words that do not appease.

A philosopher who lived alone said to her: "You are the one who passes by, your being is that which suffers, and you are going toward the Unknown from which you came."

And the shadow swallowed those sorrowful words. For a long time, the woman wept, and her moans died in the night.

Translation of a Polish Song (2)

IN order to wake you up, O Incurious One, I have crouched down in the midst of the frogs whose melancholy song charms the marsh.

But your window remained closed and you have not listened to the song of the frogs.

I have ululated like the owls whose melancholy song charms the woods by night.

But your window remained closed and you have not listened to the song of the owls.

In order to wake you up, O Incurious One, I have taken a handful of moonbeams and have thrown them like flowers at your window.

But your window remained closed and the moonbeams did not brush your insensible forehead.

I have dressed myself in snow in order to please you, and the snow burned me like the contact of your cold and virginal flesh.

But you did not open your window; you did not lean out to contemplate my bright cloak of snow.

I have covered myself with mud in order to please you, and the mud streamed over my feverish body and gripped it with its fetid odor.

But you did not open your window and you did not lean out to contemplate my abjection.

I shall take the form of your dream, O Incurious One, in order to possess you during your sleep.

I have feasted with the toads in the marshes where the snakes hiss harmoniously in order to delight us.

But I was not able to trouble you amid the illuminations of the feast.

Like the spiders I have woven webs, and I wanted to stop you in passing when you skirted the fields luminous with dew.

But you have not quit the shadow of the obstinately closed dwelling where I once went to murmur feverish words of amour to you.

And in the despair of no longer finding the savor of your lips, I have become a ghoul, and I have penetrated the darkness of tombs, and I have devoured the flesh of the dead.

Latona and Niobe

Lato and Nioba were very tender companions.

(Psappha)

IN the crepuscular times that preceded the birth of the
Moon and the Sun, two adolescent virgins with scarcely-
blossomed breasts lived side by side, Latona as blonde as
winter, Niobe as brunette as autumn. Latona's blue eyes
contained all the blue of space; Niobe's dark eyes contained
all darkness.[1]

They wandered narrowly enlaced, in the profound forests, their lips sometimes seeking one another and sometimes refusing one another, mildly frightened. The ardor
of their amity hesitated on the unknown threshold of
desire. They were wandering, equally beautiful and equally
insouciant, when they heard a sigh similar to the whisper
of the wind in foliage; and, raising their eyes, they saw a
Hamadryad leaning toward them, whose green eyes were
misted by tears.

And the two little virgins raised their eyes toward her,
filled with the same candid astonishment.

---

1 In this instance the author employs Latone [Latona] rather than the
Dorian form (Lato) of the name of the goddess also known as Leto;
this story is an anticipatory prequel to the story of Latona and Niobe
told by Ovid, with which many of Vivien's readers would have been
familiar.

"Children," she said to them—and her voice resembled the slight rustle of foliage—"I'm weeping for the inequality of your destinies. For you, Latona, will be the companion and the equal of the eternal Gods, and your glorious loins will give birth to the Moon and the Sun. The Moon, a pale virgin with green and blue vestments, will dart her mortal rays pitilessly, like silver arrows. And the implacable Sun will pierce the shadow and the silence with his mortal rays, like golden arrows. They will both be very beautiful and very cruel, and men will adore them. And you, their Mother, will stream with all their brightness and all their glory."

She interrupted herself, groaning like the wind that sobs through the branches of great oak trees.

"But you, Niobe, will feel rumbling within your being the anger and pride of the Titans, hungry for justice and thirsty for power. In you, the magnanimous revolt of the Giants is rumbling.

"And you, challenging the tyranny of the Gods who oppress the universe, will shrug off their yoke and will stand up against them, you and your predestined children.

"Your resentment will not spare the blonde companion, the joy and sweetness of your childhood, for she will share the insolent splendor of the Olympians, and will merit, like them, the lightning of your indignant eyes and the vengeful clamor of your powerful voice.

"But you will be vanquished in the unequal struggle, O rebel, and the stupor of a superhuman anguish will render you similar to the rocks eternally immobile in their fixed meditation, the arrogant rocks whose silence expresses an immutable rancor and an immutable dolor . . ."

She fell silent, as the evening breeze falls silent in the foliage, Latona and Niobe looked at one another fearfully, already seeing the will of the Gods looming up between them.

The Kiss of Selanna

I shall tell you. O attentive virgins, about the kiss that Selanna once caused to flourish on the forehead of a dead woman.

Know that Selanna is the only one among the Goddesses who has known the mystical splendor of Amour without Desire. She does not have the rigidity of Artemis and Pallas Athene, nor the ardor of Aphrodite. Her caresses are as chaste as nocturnal radiance; they brush like the invisible wings of the Soul.

One night, as Selanna was wandering through space, very pale under the shadow of her blue and green veils, she saw an abandoned dwelling that exhaled the desolation of ruins.

The royal solitude of the palace pleased her. Gently, she parted the foliage and the branches; gently, she parted the feverish flight of the bats that crowded around her; and gently, she went in.

On a funeral couch covered with silver cloth, amid lilies, tuberoses and white poppies, a virgin appeared to be asleep. But breath had forsaken her lips, devoid of color and perfume. Her eyelids resembled two faded violets. Her forehead was still luminous in the dusk of her hair, the color of ash. But she was colder and more distant than the Goddess herself.

The candle-flames had been extinct for a long time. The little abandoned dead woman reposed in the immensity of darkness . . .

Selanna, very pale under the shadow of her green and blue veils, leaned over, strangely and imperiously moved. And with her divine lips devoid of color and perfume, like the lips of the little corpse, she brushed the forehead that was still luminous in the dusk of the hair the color of ash . . .

I have told you, O attentive virgins, about the kiss that Selanna once caused to flourish on the forehead of a dead woman.

THE SHE-WOLF LADY

The She-Wolf Lady
(Narrated by M. Pierre Lenoir, 69 Rue des Dames, Paris)

I don't know why I undertook to pay court to that woman. She was neither beautiful nor pretty, nor even agreeable. And I—I say this without conceit, Mesdames—have sometimes not been looked upon indifferently. It's not that I am extraordinarily endowed by nature, physically or mentally, but in sum, such as I am—shall I confess it?—I have been spoiled by the fair sex. Oh, don't worry, I'm not going to inflict a boastful account of my conquests upon you. I'm a modest man. In any case, it's not a matter of me on this occasion. It's a matter of that woman, or rather, that young woman—in sum, that Englishwoman, whose curious face pleased me for an hour.

She was a bizarre individual. When I approached her for the first time, a large beast was asleep in the trailing folds of her skirt. I had the amiably banal words on my lips that facilitate relations between strangers. Words are nothing in such cases; the art of pronouncing them is everything . . .

But the great beast, raising its muzzle, growled in a sinister manner at the very moment when I accosted the interesting stranger.

Involuntarily, I recoiled.

"You have a nasty dog there, Mademoiselle," I observed.

"It's a she-wolf," she replied, with a certain dryness, "and as she sometimes has aversions as violent as they are inexplicable, I believe that you had better step back a little."

With a severe voice she made the she-wolf shut up: "Helga!"

I beat a retreat, slightly humiliated. It's a stupid story, you must admit. I don't know fear, but I hate ridicule. The incident annoyed me all the more because I thought I had glimpsed a gleam of sympathy in the young woman's eyes. I had certainly pleased her a little. She must have been as chagrined as me by the regrettable contretemps. What a pity! A conversation whose beginning was so promising!

I don't know why the frightful animal ceased its hostile manifestations later. I was able to approach her mistress without dread. I had never seen such a strange face. Beneath her heavy hair, of a blonde simultaneously ardent and dull, like ruddy ashes, there was the gray pallor of the complexion. The emaciated body had the fine and frail delicacy of a beautiful skeleton. (We are all a little artistic in Paris, you see.) The woman emanated an impression of rude and solitary pride, of flight and furious recoil. Her yellow eyes resembled those of her she-wolf. There was the same gaze of sly hostility. Her footfalls were so silent that they became disquieting. No one had ever walked so quietly. She was dressed in a thick fabric, which resembled fur. She was neither beautiful, nor pretty, nor charming, but, in sum, she was the only woman aboard.

I therefore paid court to her. I observed the rules most solidly established by an already long experience. She had the skill not to let me see the profound pleasure that my advances caused her. She was even able to conserve in her yellow eyes their habitual mistrustful expression. An admirable example of feminine cunning! That maneuver had the unique result of attracting me to her more violently. Long resistances sometimes give you the effect of an agreeable surprise, and render the victory more splendid. You won't contradict me on that point, will you, Messieurs? We all have very nearly the same sentiments. There is such a complete fraternity of soul between us that it renders a conversation almost impossible. That's why I often flee the monotonous company of men, who are too identical to myself.

Certainly, the lady with the she-wolf attracted me. And then—must I confess it?—the constrained chastity of floating jails exasperates my tumultuous senses. She was a woman . . .

And my court, respectful until then, became more pressing every day. I accumulated inflamed metaphors. I developed eloquent suggestions elegantly.

See how far the woman's slyness went! In listening to me, she affected a moody distraction. One might have sworn that she was uniquely interested in the foam of the wake, like fuming snow. (Women are not insensible to poetic comparisons.) But I, who have studied the psychology of the feminine visage for a long time, understood that her lowered eyelids hid vacillating glimmers of amour.

One day, I paid for my audacity. I was trying to combine flattering gesture with delicate speech when she turned toward me with a lupine bound.

"Go away," she ordered, with an almost savage decision. Her teeth were shining strangely, like those of a wild beast, her lips menacingly drawn back.

I smiled, without any anxiety. It's necessary to have a great deal of patience with women—isn't it?—and never to believe a single word that they say to you. When they order you to go, it's necessary to stay. In truth, Messieurs, I'm a little ashamed to serve you up such paltry banalities.

My interlocutrice considered me with her large yellow eyes.

"You haven't divined me. You're colliding stupidly with my invincible disdain. I neither hate nor love. I've never encountered a human being worthy of my hatred. Hatred, more patient and more tenacious than amour, needs a great adversary."

She caressed Helga's heavy head, who contemplated her with the profound eyes of a woman.

"As for amour, I'm as completely ignorant of it as you are of the art, elementary among Anglo-Saxons, of dissimulating the inherent conceit of males. If I had been a man, perhaps I might have loved a woman, for women posses the qualities I esteem: honesty in passion and forgetfulness of self in tenderness. For the most part, they are simple and sincere. They lavish themselves without restriction and without calculation. Their patience is as untiring as their generosity. They are able to forgive. They are able to wait. They possess that superior chastity, constancy."

I do not lack finesse, and I know how to take a hint. I smiled with intention at that explosion of enthusiasm. She brushed me with a distracted gaze that divined me.

"Oh, you're strangely mistaken, I've seen women very generous in mind and heart pass by, but I've never attached myself to them. Their very mildness distances them from me. I don't have a soul sufficiently elevated not to become impatient before their excess of candor and devotion."

She was beginning to annoy me with her pretentious dissertations. A prude and a bluestocking as well as a hag! But she was the only woman aboard . . . And then, she was only putting on those airs of superiority in order to render her imminent capitulation more precious.

"I only have affection for Helga, and Helga knows it. As for you, you're doubtless a good little fellow, but you can't suspect the extent to which I despise you."

She wanted to exacerbate my desire by irritating my pride. She succeeded in that, the hussy! I was red with anger and covetousness.

"Men who hasten around women, no matter who they might be, are like dogs sniffing bitches."

She darted one of her long yellow glances at me.

"I've respired the air of forests for so long, air vibrant with snow; I've so often mingled myself with vast and deserted whitenesses, that my soul has acquired something of the soul of fugitive she-wolves."

In the end, the woman frightened me. She perceived that, and changed her tone. "I have a liking for charity and freshness," she continued, with a slight laugh. "Now, the vulgarity of men repels me like the reek of garlic, and their dirtiness is as repulsive to me as the stink of drains. Men," she insisted, "are only really at home in brothels. They like prostitutes, because they find in them their own rapacity, sentimental unintelligence and cruel stupidity. They only live for interest or debauchery. Morally, they sicken me; physically, they're repugnant. I've seen men kissing women on the lips while indulging in obscene fiddling. The spectacle of a gorilla couldn't have been more repulsive."

She paused momentarily. "Even the most austere legislator only escapes by a miracle the dire consequences of the carnal promiscuities that his youth hazards. I can't understand how the least delicate woman can suffer your filthy kisses without feeling sick. In truth, my virginal scorn equals in disgust the nausea of the prostitute."

Decidedly, I thought, she's exaggerating her role, albeit well understood. She's exaggerating.

(If we were between men, Messieurs, I'd tell you that I haven't always scorned houses of ill repute, and have even picked up pitiful whores on the sidewalk many a time. That doesn't prevent Parisiennes from being more accommodating than that Saint Touch-me-not. I'm not conceited, but after all, it's necessary to be conscious of one's value.)

And, judging that the conversation had lasted long enough, I quit the Lady with the She-Wolf in a very dignified fashion. Helga followed me slyly with her long yellow gaze.

Clouds as heavy as towers were looming up on the horizon. Above them, a little glaucous sky was snaking like a liver-fluke. I had the sensation of being crushed by stone walls . . .

And the wind was getting up . . .

I was gripped by sea-sickness—I beg your pardon for this inelegant detail, Mesdames—and I was horribly indisposed. I finally went to sleep at about midnight, more lamentable than I can tell you.

At about two o'clock in the morning, I was woken up by a sinister impact, followed by an even more sinister grinding. The darkness emitted an inexpressible terror. I realized that the ship had just hit a reef.

For the first time in my life, I neglected to get dressed. I appeared on deck in a very summary costume.

A confused crowd of semi-naked men was already jostling there. They were detaching the lifeboats in great haste.

On seeing those hairy arms and legs and those hirsute chests, I couldn't help thinking, not without a smile, of something that the Lady with the She-Wolf had said: *The spectacle of a gorilla couldn't have been more repulsive . . .*

I don't know why that futile memory mocked me, in the midst of the common danger.

The waves resembled monstrous volcanoes enveloped by white smoke. Or rather, no, they didn't resemble anything. They were themselves, magnificent, terrible and mortal . . .

The wind was blowing over that immeasurable anger and exasperating it further. Salt bit my lips. I was shivering in the spray, and the din of the waves abolished all thought in me.

The Lady with the She-Wolf was there, calmer than ever—and I was fainting with terror. I saw Death looming up before me; I could almost touch her. With a bewildered gesture I touched my forehead, where I could feel the bones of the skull, sticking out frightfully. Stupidly, I started to weep . . .

I would have black and blue flesh, more bloated than a bulging bladder. The sharks would grab me here and there, by one of my disjointed limbs. And when I sank to the sea bed, crabs would climb obliquely over my putrescence and feed upon me gluttonously . . .

The wind was blowing over the sea . . .

I saw the past again. I repented of my imbecile life, my spoiled life, my doomed life. I tried to remember a benefit accorded by distraction or mistake. Had I been good for anything, useful to anyone? And my obscure conscience cried out within me, as frightful as a mute who has just miraculously recovered the power of speech: "No."

The wind was blowing over the sea . . .

I remembered vaguely the holy words that exhort repentance and promise, even at the moment of death, the salvation of the contrite sinner. I tried to rediscover, in the depths of my memory, more exhausted than an empty cup, a few words of prayer . . . and libidinous thoughts came to torment me, like red imps. I saw again the soiled beds of chance companions. I heard again their stupidly obscene appeals. I evoked embraces devoid of love. The horror of Pleasure crushed me . . .

Before the terror of the Mysterious Immensity, nothing any longer survived in me but the instinct of lust, as powerful in some people as the instinct of self-preservation. It was Life, the ugliness and vulgarity of Life, that brayed within me a ferocious protestation against annihilation . . .

The wind was blowing over the sea . . .

One has odd ideas at such moments, all the same. Me, a very honest fellow, in sum, esteemed by everyone, except a few jealous individuals, even loved by some, reproaching myself so bitterly for an existence that was neither worse nor better than anyone else's! I must have had a temporary insanity. We're all a little mad, anyway . . .

The Lady with the She-Wolf was gazing very calmly at the white waves . . . oh, whiter than snow at twilight! And, sitting on her hindquarters, Helga was howling like a bitch. She was howling lamentably, like a bitch at the moon. She *understood* . . .

I don't know why those howls chilled me even more than the noise of the wind and the waves. She was howling mortally, that diabolical she-wolf. I wanted to knock her out to make her shut up, and I looked for a plank, a spar or an iron bar—something with which to lay her out on the deck. I couldn't find anything.

The lifeboat was finally ready to depart. Men were leaping furiously toward salvation. Only the Lady with the She-Wolf didn't budge.

"Get aboard, then!" I shouted at her, installing myself in my turn. She approached without haste, followed by Helga.

"Mademoiselle," interjected the lieutenant who was commanding us as best he could, "we can't take that animal with us. There are only places here for people."

"I'll stay, then," she said, stepping back.

Frightened men were rushing forward, uttering incoherent cries. We were obliged to let her draw away.

For myself, I really couldn't be bothered with such a silly girl. She had been so insolent in my regard! You understand that, don't you, Messieurs? You wouldn't have acted any differently.

In sum, I was safe, or very nearly. Dawn had broken—and my God, what a dawn! There was a shiver of paralyzed light, a gray stupor, a swarm of larval things in a twilight of limbo . . .

And we saw the blue tint of distant land . . .

Oh, the joy and relief of perceiving welcoming and sure ground!

Since that horrible experience I've only made one voyage by sea, in order to come back here. I won't get caught again, for sure.

I must not be very egotistical, Mesdames. In the midst of the indescribable uncertainty in which I was struggling, and although I'd narrowly escaped Destruction, I still had the courage to take an interest in the fate of my companions in misfortune. The second lifeboat had been submerged by the frenetic assault of too large a number of demented individuals. I watched it sink, with horror. The Lady with the She-Wolf had taken refuge on a broken mast, a piece of floating wreckage, along with the submissive beast. I was certain that, if the strength and endurance of that woman did not betray her, she might be saved. I wanted that with all my heart. But the cold, the slowness and fragility of that improvised craft, devoid of sails and a rudder, fatigue and feminine weakness . . . !

They were only a short distance from land when the Lady, exhausted, turned to Helga as if to say: "I'm finished . . ."

And then something dolorous and solemn happened. The she-wolf, *which had understood*, prolonged her howl of despair toward the nearby and inaccessible land. Then, standing up, she put her forepaws on the shoulders of her mistress, who took her in her arms. They both sank beneath the waves . . .

The Sniggering Thirst
(Narrated by Jim Nicholls)

"WHAT a strange sunset!" I said to Polly. We were riding on our mules, exhausted by lassitude and heat.

"Imbecile!" muttered my companion. "Can't you see that the glow is in the east?"

"In that case, it must be dawn. I must be drunk—and yet, I haven't had a drink all day."

The somnolent march of the mules was lulling my thoughts agreeably.

We were in the middle of the prairie. In front of us was a desert of pale grass. Behind us was an ocean of pale grass. Around us, Thirst was prowling. I could see her dry lips moving.[1] Polly, the bitch with straw-colored hair, couldn't see her, which wasn't astonishing. Polly had never been able to see further than the end of her nose, red in the open air and the sun.

I turned in my saddle, tugging the reins forcefully.

"Why are you stopping?" Polly asked me.

"I'm looking at Thirst. Her robe is as gray as the dry grass out there. She's grimacing. She's sniggering. The

---

1 The noun *soif* [thirst] has the feminine gender in French (like *mort* [death]).

contortions of her carcass are scaring me. She's very ugly, Thirst."

Polly shrugged her heavy shoulders.

"You're mad, Jim. It's only simpletons of your kind who have nightmares in broad daylight like that."

I would gladly have given her a kick or a punch, but reiterated and painful experiences had convinced me that Polly's physical vigor far surpassed mine. I only had a vague mental superiority over her. And even then, my companion's common sense had often got me out of a spot of trouble, when my crackbrained divagations wouldn't have been able to do so. I had received the education, it's true, but what use is education in the prairies? A good revolver is much more valuable out there.

Polly's hair was implacably flamboyant in the light. I had a desire to scalp her, like my friends and adversaries the Indians, in order to splatter that blonde mane with blood. Why? I don't know. There are ideas that occur to you like that in the prairies.

I looked at her brown cheeks, which resembled two baked apples. I don't know why I thought at that moment about a thin, very pale face that I had once loved. I evoked the shadow of a little house, the coolness of closed blinds and the lovely eyelids of a woman who was reading. How charming she was, with her eyelids lowered! I adored the shadow of lashes over white cheeks. Ah . . . !

I didn't know the métier of a prairie-runner then. I hadn't encountered the bitch with the straw-colored hair.

Why had I quit the little house full of shade and the green light of closed shutters? I don't know.

I don't know, either, whether the strange little girl who read for long hours is alive or dead. I think she must be dead, because I sometimes have such a great void in my heart.

But I'm not sure of anything.

It disturbs your ideas a little to have seen at close range the Thirst that prowls in the prairies.

I had chosen that Polly, whom I execrated, as my traveling companion—or rather, she had chosen me. I'll end up killing her one day; that I know. I hate her because she's vigorously healthy, and I'm feverish and debilitated. She's bolder and more robust than a male. She could send me sprawling ten meters away with a flick. She's a good ogress, though, when she hasn't drunk too much. But there you go! She willingly gets drunk. Perhaps she too is afraid of the Thirst that is lying in wait for both of us.

I hazarded a reflection as we went along.

"There'll surely be a storm before long, Polly, my enchantress, my chimera."

"Idiot!" she breathed, with conviction. "Leave me alone. You only ever say stupid things. Of course there'll be a storm before long. That's visible and tangible, and I don't like unnecessary words."

"O my admirable sweetness, your wisdom is as benevolent as it is profound."

She didn't deign to reply. I'll surely end up killing her one day. I'd never have the strength to strangle her, but I'll shoot her in the back with my revolver. That way, it would be finished and I wouldn't have to think about her any longer. Perhaps Thirst will draw away from me when I've slaked her with blood. Who knows?

The supernatural dawn was increasing in intensity. We stopped when dusk fell. Polly poured me out, from her bulging water-skin, a drop of firewater. I drank to her imminent death. Suddenly, the bitch stopped drinking.

That astonished me a little. Only something extraordinary could distract Polly like that from the extreme satisfaction she obtained from her favorite beverage.

"What's the matter?" I asked, with an affectionate interest.

Polly doesn't, in fact, like unnecessary words; I'll render her that justice. Long marches in the sun have rendered her taciturn. She really is the companion a man of the prairies needs. She simply showed me a little ash mingled with the gray grass.

I understood her thought. My eyes turned instinctively toward the strange dawn reddening in the east. But a small hill prevented me from seeing what was happening out there.

Polly muttered a muffled oath. My knees buckled under me. She looked me up and down with her disdainful gaze and, quitting me without a word, she set about climbing the hill.

I followed her, for fear of the solitude, even more odious than that detestable companion.

Having arrived at the summit, we were breathless.

From the north to the south, the entire horizon was ablaze.

A prairie fire!

A wind of flame that was coming toward us with the velocity of a simoom or a sirocco, sweeping the desert of dry grass in the blink of an eye—and nothing in its passage that could stop it!

I shivered, like a sick man dying of fever. Polly wasn't afraid.

I forgot my anguish momentarily, in the rage of not seeing her teeth chatter. Her terror would almost have soothed my own fear. But she's brave, much braver than I am. She didn't go pale, because nothing in the world, neither death not the trumpet of the Last Judgment would make her go pale. She has, moreover, a ruddy complexion. Me, I was yellower than a guinea.

We returned in all haste to our improvised camp, where were had left our mules grazing, rendered umbrageous by fear.

The evening breeze was pushing the hurricane of flames toward us.

I don't fear death, but pain frightens me. The prospect of being roasted alive, clawed me in an acute fashion. Even Polly had a grave expression, although her nerves are more robust than the tendons of an ox.

Roasted alive in the prairie . . . !

The fire was advancing like an immense lightning flash. I was astonished by the rapidity of its progress. A few more minutes, and we'd both be charcoal. A few more minutes and . . .

It was beautiful, all the same, that whirlwind of flames. It was more beautiful than the sun. I had never seen anything as magnificent. It was so marvelously splendid that I fell to my knees and extended my arms toward the Fire, laughing as little children and idiots laugh.

I repeat that it was as frightful as it was superb, and that I almost went mad in consequence. It was too beautiful for human eyes. God alone could have looked that conflagration in the face without dying or losing his reason.

But Polly, who has no more soul than my mules, didn't understand, and looked without seeing. She isn't astonished by anything, she doesn't admire anything . . .

I hated her for not being afraid. Oh, how I hated her! I hate her ferociously, because she's stronger and more valiant than me. I hate her as a woman execrates the man who dominates her. I'll certainly end up killing her one day, quite simply for the pleasure of vanquishing her . . .

"Let's not waste time," said Polly, resolutely, in her everyday voice, neither a semitone higher or lower. Oh, how I hated her for being so calm! She crouched down, and in the blink of an eye, she set fire to the grass in front of her.

I thought for a second that she had gone mad as well; and I howled with joy, like an Indian avenging himself.

She was undisturbed. She was used to my eccentric humor. She was too scornful of me to fear me.

"The fire will fight the fire, Jim."

We retreated. Our fire was burning quietly, like the benevolent fire of placid hearths. The other fire, nourished by thousands of leagues of devoured grass, was advancing like a tidal wave of light and sound.

I closed my eyes, drunk on smoke. When I opened them again, everything around us was black. It was the ruins of the conflagration. The furnace was miraculously extinct.

Fire had vanquished Fire.

Polly was standing proudly before me, her fists on her hips. What rendered me furious was that she hadn't been afraid for a single second.

She won't be any more afraid on the day when I kill her, because she doesn't fear death. She doesn't fear God either.

She looked at me without flinching.

"What a coward you are," she said, disdainfully,

Prince Charming
(Narrated by Gesa Karoly)

I promised you, curious girl, to tell you the true story of Sarolta Andrassy. You knew her, didn't you? You remember her black hair, with blue and red reflections, and her amorous, imploring and melancholy eyes.

Sarolta lived in the country with her aged mother. They had the Szechenys for neighbors, who had just quit Budapest definitively.[1] A bizarre family, in truth! One might have mistaken Bela Szecheny for a little girl, and his sister Terka for a young boy. Curiously enough, Bela possessed all the feminine virtues and Terka all the masculine faults. Bela's hair was greenish blond, Terka's, more vivid, rosy blonde. The brother and the sister resembled one another strangely, which is very rare among members of the same family, whatever anyone says.

Bela's mother had not yet resigned herself to cutting the little boy's blond curls and exchanging his gracious muslin or velvet skirts for vulgar short trousers. She pampered him

---

1 These characters are fictitious, but the author presumably appropriated this name from the great Hungarian statesman Istvan Szechenyi (1791-1860); one of his three children was named Bela. Andrassy is also the surname of an ancient Hungarian family, which included numerous statesmen.

like a girl. As for Terka, she grew in her own fashion, like a wild plant. She lived in the open air, marauding, pillaging kitchen gardens, insupportable and at war with everyone. She was a child devoid of tenderness and expansion. Bela, on the contrary, was sweetness personified. His adoration for his mother was manifest in affection and incessant caresses. Terka did not like anyone, and nobody liked her.

Sarolta came to the Szechenys' house one day. Her amorous eyes were imploring in her thin pale face. Bela pleased her a great deal and they played together for a long time. Terka prowled around them with a grim expression. When Sarolta spoke to her, she fled.

She might have been pretty, that incomprehensible Terka, but she was too tall for her age, too thin, too gauche, too gangling. Whereas Bela was so dainty and so gentle!

The Szechenys left Hungary a few months later. Sarolta wept bitterly for her playmate. On the advice of a physician, his mother had taken him to Nice, as well as his recalcitrant little sister. Bela had an excessively delicate chest. He was, in any case, not very robust.

In her dreams, Sarolta always invoked the excessively frail and excessively pretty child whose memory persisted in her. And she said to herself, smiling at the blond image: "If I have to marry later, I'd like to marry Bela."

Several years past—oh, how slowly for the impatient Sarolta! Bela must have reached the age of twenty, and Terka seventeen. They were still on the Riviera. And Sarolta was desolate in those joyless years, solely illuminated by the illusion of a dream.

She was dreaming at her window on a violet evening when her mother came to tell her that Bela had returned.

110

Sarolta's heart sang as if to burst. And the next day, Bela came to see her. He was the same, and even more charming than before. Sarolta was glad that he had retained the effeminate and gentle manner that had always pleased her so much. He was still the same fragile child . . . but that child now possessed an inexpressible grace. Sarolta searched in vain for the cause of that transformation, which rendered him so attractive. His voice was musical and distant like a mountain echo. She admired everything about him, even his stone-gray English suit and his mauve cravat.

Bela contemplated the young woman with his changed eyes, his strangely beautiful eyes, eyes that did not resemble those of other men . . .

"How thin he is!" observed Sarolta's mother, after his departure. "He must still be in very delicate health, the poor boy."

Sarolta did not reply. She closed her eyes in order to see Bela again behind her closed eyelids. How pretty, pretty, pretty he was!

He came back the next day, and every day. He was the Prince Charming who is only revealed through the infantile pages of fairy tales. She could not look him in the face without swooning ardently, languidly . . .

Her face varied in accordance with the expression of the desired face. Her heart beat in accordance with the beat of that other heart. Unconscious and puerile tenderness had become amour.

Bela went pale as soon as she came in, diaphanous in her white summer dress. He sometimes gazed at her without speaking, like someone meditating before a faultless statue. Sometimes he took her by the hand. She thought she was touching the hand of an invalid, the palm was so hot and dry. A little fever rose to Bela's cheeks then.

One day, she asked him for news of the undisciplined Terka.

"She's still in Nice," he replied, negligently. And they talked about something else. Sarolta understood that Bela did not love his sister. Moreover, that was not astonishing. Such a taciturn and grim child!

What had to happen happened. Bela asked for her hand in marriage a few months later. He had entered his twenty-first year. His mother did not oppose the union.

There was an unreal betrothal, as delicate as the white roses that Bela brought every day. There were prayers more fervent than poems, and the frisson of souls on lips. The nuptial dream passed through the profundity of silences.

"Why," said Sarolta to her fiancé, "are you more worthy to be loved than other young men? Why do you have a tenderness unknown to them? Where have you learned the divine words that they never pronounce?"

The ceremony was held in absolute intimacy. The candles heightened the roseate gleams in Bela's blond hair. The incense drifted toward him, and the thunder of the organ exalted and glorified him. For the first time since the commencement of the world, the groom was as beautiful as the bride.

They departed toward the blue shores where the desire of lovers is exasperated. They were seen, a divine couple, the eyelashes of the one brushing the eyelids of the other. They were seen, amorously and chastely enlaced, the black hair of the wife spread over the blonde hair of the husband,

But this, curious girl, is where the story becomes a little difficult to tell. A few months later, the veritable Bela

Szecheny reappeared. He was not Prince Charming, alas. He was only a pretty boy, nothing more. He searched furiously for the identity of the young usurper, and he learned that the usurper in question was his sister Terka.

Sarolta and Prince Charming have never returned to Hungary. They are hiding in the depths of a Venetian palace or a Florentine house. And sometimes one encounters them, like a vision of ideal tenderness, amorously and chastely enlaced.

The Sisters of Silence

I have heard mention, in terms that were sometimes eloquent and sometimes scornful, of the laic monastery created by the dolor of a woman for the dolor of other women. It was, assured some, a fraternal and sacred place in which lassitudes steeped themselves in meditation. Others only saw it as the unhealthy caprice of an individual gone astray in mourning.

I resolved to see and learn, and one autumn day, I went to the profane convent.

The Superior welcomed me with a taciturn grace. Everything about her was a gray harmony: her hair and her twilight eyes and the melancholy folds of her robe.

"May I know . . . ?" I commenced, embarrassed and awkward.

"Don't interrogate me," interjected the Gray Woman, not without softness, "for questioning is a brutal violation of the right and the duty to be silent. Watch and observe, learn for yourself, without ever asking anything of another fallible individual, as uncertain as you are."

And this is what I saw and learned in that strange laic monastery created by the dolor of a woman for the dolor of other women.

The monastery was pale in the middle of an immense garden where only virginal white flowers shed their petals, the flowers of sterility and death. Only the youngest among the recluses were authorized to lavish on plants and foliage the delicate cares for which gardeners habitually take responsibility. For, according to the convent's rule, the vulgar hand of a man must not soil the flowers.

The most mystical silence reigned in the convent. Those who were still tormented by the memory of speech came, at rare intervals, to the *parloir*,[1] where they resumed, for a few minutes, the vain practice of human language. Then they recovered, with a placid joy, the monastic Dream.

The ceremonies of that house of isolation and repose took place in dolorous sunsets. The young women with fluid tresses murmured verses or intoned chants. A few fervent solitaries wandered through the galleries, their gazes enchained by the splendor of paintings and statues. Others picked the pale flowers of the hothouses and gardens, or lingered in contemplation of the infinity of the dusk and the sea.

Like an eagle's nest, the pious abode huddled amid the crags. Passers-by feared the violence of its perfumes. Once, the inexorable breath of orange-blossom had caused a virgin to die.

At the foot of the monastery, the abyss was blue-tinted, more attractive than the waters of the Mediterranean. The

---

1 The *parloir* of a nineteenth-century French convent was a special room set aside for the visitors who came, frequently or infrequently, to see the children committed to the educational care of the nuns, or the nuns themselves; the literal translation of the term is, of course, "speaking place." It was transcribed into English as "[servants'] parlour" in the days when that referred to the one room in an aristocratic house where the servants could speak freely among themselves. The

windows were broad, and, always wide open over the sea, they contained the entire glorious curve of the rainbow. When the organ spread the tempest of its thunder and lightning, when the violins sobbed all divine anguish, the waves mingled the eternity of their monotonous rhythm with the hymns.

The youngest Sister came to me like the incarnation of my most beautiful thought. Her robe was the same violet as the evening. The woman evoked for me the fragility of nacre and the aristocratic sadness of black swans in an obscure wake. Responding to my silence, she murmured:

"I've searched in that shadow, not for peace, as the Exile knocks on the door of the monastery, but for Infinity."

And I saw that her visage resembled the divine visage of Solitude.

The Cruelty of Precious Stones
(Narrated by Giuseppe Bianchini)[1]

IN truth, Madonna Gemma, you are well named. You are the dazzling and insensible sister of precious stones. I love the aquamarines that are the same color as your eyes. Aquamarines are the most beautiful of all gems. They have the cold limpidity of winter waves.

How you love the jewels that ornament you, O my very beautiful Lady! Their dormant life mingles with your breath and the calm beat of your arteries. Oh, the pearls that espouse your neck are voluptuous and cruel! Oh, the profundity of those emeralds and the frisson of those opals!

Do you remember why I once plunged myself for such long months amid parchments and crucibles? I wanted to discover the Philosopher's Stone for you. I wanted gold, gold and more gold, a stream of gold in your lap. Your body would have buckled under the burden of adornments. The splendor of your necklaces and your rings would have humiliated the Dogaressa. The prow of your gondola would have been a blinding dazzle of rubies, leaving reflections of autumn sunlight in the water . . .

How you sparkle in the shadows! Turn your beryl eyes

---

1 Obviously not the great scholar Guiseppe Bianchini (1704-1764).

away from me. Your implacable soul is smiling in your gaze, Madonna . . .

There are bizarre and terrible men who enchant the physical dolor of others. The cries and contortions of tortures sharpen their weary sensualities. You resemble them, you who find the ugliness of corporeal suffering and the barbarity of bloodshed repugnant. Your joy is to reanimate the anguish slumbering in souls. The vision of my fears and my tortures reddens through my words. That is why you are listening to the story of them with such a bright smile. You are implacable, Madonna Gemma; but you are so beautiful that I will obey you.

My laborious nights as an alchemist gave birth to the strange humor that pleases you and displeases you in me. Oh, those laborious nights! I sensed vaguely that someone was spying on my secret studies. You know that as well as I do, perhaps better than me. Someone whose invisible eyes were watching me denounced me to the Inquisition. I was accused of black magic. By whom? Perhaps you know, Madonna. Perhaps you know that in consequence of a denunciation I was cloistered in a tenebrous prison seven years ago.

How can I depict the horrors of that dungeon without daylight? But my most burning torture was seeing my patient studies interrupted just as I was about to discover the Philosopher's Stone. A few hours more, and I would have reigned over all the gold and all the gems in the world.

For I long time I dreamed with the intolerable fixity of the damned. You appeared to me in a flash of precious stones. I loved you with an inexpressible hatred. You showed me with a gesture the iron door, the bars of the window and the bolts. During the night, my tortures were even more demonic. Fever and Dementia carried me away like a sirocco. I sank in an ocean of darkness.

And, in order to catch up with you—don't tremble thus, my dazzling Mistress—in order to find you again and to torture you expertly with the infinite caresses of cruelty, I wanted to escape from that tenebrous prison.

One evening, greener than an April river, the jailer came in with a grinding of rusty iron. He considered me with a jovial scorn. I had always shown myself meeker than a suckling mule. I had the tearful submission of a beaten child.

He asked me whether the fever was relenting slightly. I responded with groans, and mingled my plaints with protestations of gratitude for the interest he testified to me.

He headed for the door after a few stupid words of encouragement. With a furious bound I seized him from behind and bit the nape of his neck ferociously. The shock was so great that he fell backwards without uttering a cry. With one hand I gagged him with the straw of my dungeon. Then, seizing the heavy bunch of keys that hung from his belt, I hit him over the head with it vigorously.

He took a long time to die, and I became impatient more than once before finally seeing the trickle of blood that carried away the debris of his brain.

I found the hideousness of the spectacle slightly repulsive, but the man was too stupid for me to linger over deploring his loss. I stripped him and, having hidden my bloodstained garments under the ample cloak that he wore habitually, I traversed the somber corridors.

A hoarse, drunken voice stopped me, chilled by sweat and trembling more than a Romagnol afflicted with malaria.

"Hurry up, Beppo! The soup's fuming on the table."

119

In one of the divinations that extreme terror sometimes brings, I understood that the jailer's wife was about to give me away.

I turned round. In the blink of an eye I had discovered everything. I immediately observed that she was abominably drunk. Her breasts were dangling over her belly, which was swollen as if by pregnancy, like two empty bags. The reek of cheap wine emerged from her thick lips. Her hair, inexpertly dyed, was red in patches. Large gold rings weighed down her ears, more accustomed to hearing the bellowing of pole-axed beasts than serenades. She was staggering, and sour hiccups were escaping from her throat.

What struck me above all was the vulgar coquetry of her garments. Her scarlet skirt was as flamboyant as a forge. Her bellicose yellow blouse was as loud as the trumpets of victory. Several rows of coral were wrapped round her fat, short neck, easy to squeeze between my murderous hands. Such necks are predestined to strangulation, as certain long and pale fragilities are to rape.

A plan, as irreflective as an instinct, sprang to my delirious mind. I fell at the enormous peasant woman's knees. "Madonna," I sighed, with the emphasis of a sentimental clown, "forgive an overly fervent adorer for the ruse that has gained him the enormous fortune of penetrating as far as you."

She considered me, her groin wide open and her brain blurred by tavern vintages.

"Have no fear, O red-haired beauty, incarnation of an autumn sunset! I have locked your husband in an empty cell, after having manhandled him a little. I've stuffed straw in his mouth, as one does to donkeys, which resemble him. Thus gagged, he won't be able to interrupt our amorous conversation."

I kissed her kneecaps courageously. Her vacillating pupils dilated with astonishment and alarm.

A rapid thought traversed my mind. At the moment when I was arrested I had mounted a delicate ring for you: two sirens, sculpted in green, with enameled scales and hair, holding in their upturned arms an aquamarine as beautiful as a drop of glacial sea-water. I had succeeded in concealing that jewel. I offered it to the creature, whose dugs were shaken by a convulsive tremor.

"I've forged this ring for you, O radiance of my dreams!"

A smile of unconscious bliss broadened her heavy drinker's lips.

"Yesterday evening, when the first stars caused the dead water of an illusory life to quiver, I hid in the shadows and I sang passionate canzoni for you."

"I remember," sighed the drunkard, swooning with pleasure as if a hand had tickled her expertly. "Oh, yes, I heard that beautiful baritone voice that rose so amorously toward me—but I thought I recognized the accent of the gondolier who has been courting my daughter Giuseppina for three months."

"When the dawn opened like a rose, I was still under your window. I composed fervent litanies in your honor, as to the Holy Virgin. You are the flame of Venice, the mirage of the setting sun, the smile of dull waves, and in my dreams I have named you Violante."

"My name is Onesta," the horrible witch interjected, flattering her overflowing dugs complaisantly.

"I'll confess everything to you, Onesta mia. I am a great lord whose palace will open its triumphal doors wide for you. Your feet of an errant child will be reflected in marble of almost diaphanous purity, a wave carrying snow. Listen, Onesta. A robe of silver cloth in which pearls are shining will follow the melodious line of your hips. Aquamarines wedded to moonstones will give you the illusion of starlight over the sea. Two maidservants will bear the regal weight of your train, heavy with metal and precious stones, and two enamored pages will sing, by turns, kneeling before your armchair, the tender verses that I shall dictate to them. I shall not offer you flowers, my charmer, for it is necessary that your eyes are not saddened by the agony of a rose. You shall only contemplate the eternal beauty of opals and emeralds. And into onyx cups I shall pour wines as glorious as victories, as sweet as poisons and as vehement as kisses . . ."

On hearing mention of wines, my tottering conquest drooled with joy. A gleam traversed her haggard eyes.

"Wine!" she sighed.

"Let me take you away, Onesta," I begged. "Follow me to the palace of amour, where the nuptial couch is already prepared. I'm a magician, and I know strange caresses that the perverse archangels have taught me."

I stopped in order to savor the effect produced by my eloquence. Then, knowing that women prefer precise gestures to the most sumptuous promises, I leaned over. With my breath, slightly deprived of savor by the strict regime of the prison, I brushed Onesta's red neck. Seeing the encouraging somersaults of all that Chianti-impregnated flesh, I was emboldened to certain expert touches that provoked further hiccups. I continued, insinuating and tempting:

"I shall teach you the red spice of bites. I shall teach you the insistence of lips and the slow tenacity of hands. Your boor of a husband has doubtless left you ignorant of those things . . ."

I spoke to her intimately: "Come, Onesta."

She fixed her stupid eyes upon me.

"You do indeed have the speech and manners of a great lord," she stammered, "but I can't leave my husband and children for you."

"Could your husband, like me, adorn your womanly splendor magnificently? Would he be able to select the precious stones that reflect your eyes? And you are too gracious only to be a mother, Onesta."

"Perhaps all that is true," the harpy acquiesced, very romantically drunk.

"It is as true as naked Verity," I insisted. "Come, Onesta mia."

The shadows of dusk were deepening. A musical softness was making the air vibrate like the taut strings of a cithara.

Suddenly, I shuddered. We heard resounding footsteps approaching. My ignoble companion was on the point of fainting. I seized her arm violently, and, as brutal as a carter whipping his beast, I ordered her to follow me. She obeyed, more passive than the livestock.

It was a jailer, whose massive frame we could barely make out in the corridor blurred by twilight. I had a tremor of hot fever when he called to us "Are you going to breathe the evening air on the canal?"

Onesta stammered: "My husband is suffering a little, Jacopo. We're both going to bed. Goodnight."

"Goodnight," said the man, who went on his way, humming.

We arrived at the main gate. In response to Onesta's strangled request, the guard opened the grille and let us out into the blue penumbra . . .

The south wind was carrying aromatic memories and I know not what evil lusts. The lagoon was as warm and perverse as a gaping vagina. I caressed Onesta's dugs distractedly.

"There's a gondola, my pensive beauty. Deign to follow me all the way to the palace of my amorous dreams."

She embarked, drowned in a happy stupor. I know how to steer a boat as easily as torturing a woman, Gemma. I took the place of the slightly bewildered gondolier and reassured the worthy fellow by slipping him one of the few old coins that the rapacity of the jailers had spared.

We allowed ourselves to be drawn along the bewitching canal. Oh, the cruelty of nocturnal waters!

A dwelling with gaping doors trailed its yellow and red lights over the waters. The music of mandolins and hoarse guitars floated as far as us. It was coming from a brothel frequented by sailors and gondoliers.

"Come, my immortal Lady. There is Asti spumante in closed rooms . . ."

We went in. A pestilential reek of garlic and bad wine suffocated me as soon as the threshold.

I closed the curtains over our imminent amours. Onesta was already slipping into a stupid somnolence.

I thought about her awakening. When drink was no longer fermenting in her empty brain, what alarms would dilate her imbecile pupils? She would denounce me. And if I abandoned her immediately, trusting in her torpor, there was a risk that a light of reason might return.

And why not admit it? The cruelty of the waters and the night was within me. Mortal lust rendered me similar to a wild beast in folly. I threw myself upon the abominable drunkard and used her with a frenzy that your most complex kisses had not accorded me, Gemma. The furious pleasure made me sob faintly, like a plaintive infant. And I bruised those abject lips with bites.

But a stronger covetousness assailed me. I profited from the stupor in which my companion was bogged down, sunk by the intensity of the spasm, and, seizing her throat forcefully, I strangled her, delightedly. Certain fat short necks are predestined to strangulation . . .

Onesta's death-throes were brief, even too brief. Weighed down by wine, weakened by sexual convulsions, she succumbed without delay between my vigorous hands. I know how to strangle as expertly as to caress.

The hideous grotesquerie of the cadaver was such that I started to laugh. Carnal appeasement rendered me very mild. The male in me was satisfied. A victim had been immolated to the cruelty of the waters and the night. I left, my soul serene.

"Why are you leaving your companion there," asked a maidservant who was teasing a sailor.

"She's too drunk to get up. She's sleeping as profoundly as the dead in their coffins."

And I smiled innocently at that pleasantry, of which I alone could appreciate the delicate savor.

The waters of the night approved, and enveloped me with an indulgent softness. I spat on the reflections of the stars and sang my most beautiful sea shanties.

An hour went by, diaphanous and light. The reflections of the stars were extinguished in the depths of the lagoon. Then, as triumphant as a clarion call, dawn burst forth, stridently.

I doubled the cape of the Dogana and followed the Giudecca canal. The rocking of the gondola provided rhythm to my tranquil dreams. The green water had the perfidious languor of your somnolent eyes, Madonna . . .

The gondola stopped outside your door. In spite of the rising sun, your house was dormant in the shadow of slumber. A perfume of indolence and belated dreams rose toward me. I headed for your bedroom.

You were asleep. Your marble attitude chilled me. I shivered before your eyelids, devoid of palpitation. The darkness marbled your forehead and rendered it similar to the blue-tinted brow of a corpse.

I advanced, my hands joined. I shivered in all my paralyzed limbs. Slowly, very slowly, Gemma mia, you opened your eyes. And I read in the depths of your haggard pupils a terror so monstrous that *I understood*. I knew what invisible gaze had lain in ambush while I was toiling among my crucibles and my parchments. I knew what hand had traced the perfidious lines that denounced me to the Inquisition. I knew who had betrayed me, by virtue of the curiosity of evil . . .

And it is since that day that you have loved me, Gemma mia. You love me with all your terror. Your lassitude of body and soul only knows a quivering awakening under the impact of terror. And because you fear me, you love me. You're not unaware that I'll break you later, at the whim of my caprice. You're not unaware that I'll destroy you, when you've ceased to please me. Silent with passive horror, you keep watch on my gestures and footsteps. You're waiting for The End. But the moment hasn't yet come, for your body tempts me like the perfumed juice of watermelons and the pulp of ripe figs. Your hour has not yet sounded, Madonna Gemma . . .

I want your lips. Kisses, kisses, kisses . . .

Treason in the Forest
(Narrated by Blue Dirk)

I am not a wicked man, although I've been nicknamed the Forest Devil. People also call me Blue Dirk, because I'm tattooed all over my body. Joan also had blue tattoos. Joan was my wife. We weren't married according to the Anglican Church, because there was no clergyman where we were, but she was my wife even so.

She had the most beautiful tattoos that a woman can covet. No American Indian woman is more expertly decorated with tomahawks and turtles. On the right leg I'd designed a devil with the horns of a buffalo and a cow's tail. On the right wrist there was a snake by way of a bracelet, and on the left breast, two hearts united by a single arrow, and our interlaced initials.

I have no idea why I've been nicknamed the Forest Devil. It's true that I'm a trifle nasty when I'm drunk. I've killed a few men without knowing it, while I was drunk, and I've even knocked down two or three women who resisted me because, rendered amorous by eau-de-vie, I wanted to do them violence. But I wouldn't have acted that way if I hadn't been drinking. It's also true that I took a little girl by force, but that was because I'd been wandering in the solitudes for a month without seeing a woman, however ugly or old. I assure you that I wouldn't have acted in that fashion if I hadn't been fasting terribly. It was only a little lust. And then the child cried too loudly. I left, after gratifying her with a sharp slap. I don't like crying, myself. Children ought never to make a noise. I burned the feet of an old farmer's wife who didn't want to tell me where she'd buried her money, but as she ended up revealing the hidey hole where the savings were, I didn't do her any more harm. Fundamentally, I'm an excellent fellow. That odor of cooked flesh was, in any case, unbearable. In sum, all that's not of much importance, and I don't know why they call me the Forest Devil.

What is murder, after all? An advance of a few years on the inevitable end. Is twenty minutes of torture so terrible, then? Isn't it a thousand times less hideous than long years of agony? A cancer, for example . . . personally, I'd rather be murdered than die of cancer . . .

If I'd sent to the other world a being who, without my intervention, would have been immortal, I'd surely have a heavy burden on my conscience.

As for the affair of the little girl, I only anticipated the natural violence that another male, in all probability, would have exercised on her person. I've never possessed a nubile virgin, but it's been affirmed to me that the initiation is always very painful for a woman. So, a little later, she would certainly have known the brutality of a man.

It's true that there are a great many women who die virgins. In spite of that, I've heard it said that that isn't the normal destiny of a woman. It even appears that it's almost immoral. The people who have told me that have what people call "healthy ideas." Having healthy ideas means thinking like everyone else.

Perhaps I was wrong to roast the feet of the old farmer's wife. But why was she so avaricious? If I've been able to cure her of her miserliness, I've rendered her a great service. Perhaps I've facilitated her entry into the Kingdom of Heaven.

I am, fundamentally, an excellent fellow. I'll give you a proof of it. When the inhabitants of a little Hindu village ravaged by two tigers came to ask for my help, I went to their aid right away. In truth, they had offered me a superb recompense for ridding them of those two accursed beasts, but I assure you that love of my neighbor was the motive determining my beautiful enterprise.

Joan was with me . . . an admirable hunting companion. That's why I kept her for so long.

Thanks to one of the rare villagers that had escaped the claws of the tiger and the tigress, we discovered the beasts' preferred lair. We attached a white calf to a tree nearby, and the following day, Joan and I set off on the adventure.

We took a kullal with us—that's a wine-merchant—who filled the double role of guide and water-carrier, as well as Mankari the clear-eyed, my principal shikari, Sala and Nursoo, two other beaters a few years younger.

We'd been walking for a few miles when we heard the tiger's magnificent roar. Joan shivered, almost voluptuously. Her eyes dilated with enthusiasm and pride. We had to combat an adversary worthy of us.

"*Wu hai!*" lamented the kullal, who was trembling in all his bronze-colored limbs. "That's the sahib of my village! That's the king of the country!"

His abject terror increased from one moment to the next.

Sensing that he was getting ready to run madly, Joan said to him with her habitual phlegm: "If you try to flee, the tiger will certainly have your skin, old chap. I advise you to stay behind us; it's your only chance of salvation."

Mankali and Joan advanced first. Joan had the eyes of a lynx. We reached a few rocks from which the sacrificed calf could be seen.

"Look!" Joan whispered.

I looked. Through the twilight I could only see a motionless white mass.

"The calf is dead," observed Mankali in a low voice.

Joan contented herself with wagging her index finger rhythmically.

"Its tail is still moving," agreed Nursoo, the youngest shikari. He had understood my wife's pantomime.

"Can you see the tiger?" I asked Joan.

She nodded her head. Widening my eyes, I finally made out the body of the predator.

Ah! The superb beast!

Joan started walking rapidly. I followed her. The tiger was so occupied devouring the unfortunate white calf alive that it didn't hear us coming. We sheltered behind a tree, twenty yards from the tiger.

The calf's neck plunged into the maw of the handsome monster, whose paws were clutching its victim cruelly.

"Don't take aim yet," Joan recommended. "It's necessary not to wound it without killing it."

With a supreme effort, the calf struggled. The movement that its adversary made then to seize it again uncovered the pale target of its belly and its breast. It had turned on to its left side. I aimed at the heart and, slightly anxious, I fired.

With a magnificent bound it rolled over, its mouth agape, its breath panting. Joan approached the dying beast and finished it off with the butt of her rifle, breaking the vertebral column.

The kullal's teeth were chattering. Joan, whom that shivering cowardice irritated beyond all measure, took him by the arm impatiently.

"Come and see it at close range," she said, pointing at the dead tiger. "It's a fine beast."

But the terrified kullal only responded with frightened moans. Joan's lips pursed with an inexpressible disdain.

"Old man," she said, putting her rude murderer's hand on my shoulder, "our work isn't finished. It's necessary that the tigress goes to join the tiger."

"You're right, Joan."

She didn't take away the hand that was weighing on my shoulder. For the first time in my life I saw her hesitate and her expression darken before the task.

"It won't be easy," she said, very slowly. "It's stupid, if you wish, but I have an idea that it'll give us trouble. Tigresses are much more to be feared than tigers, Dirk. They're more ferocious and more perfidious."

"Do you think you're teaching me my métier? But come on, you aren't afraid? It would be the first time. But if you're baulking at the task . . ."

"You know full well, imbecile, that I'm not afraid of death. Since it's necessary to disappear somehow, it's better to go in the open air, young and strong, than to rot gradually in a sickroom, where one chokes, and which stinks. And the drugs, pooh! But I have an idea that the tigress will give us trouble."

She contemplated the beautiful calm forest. The branches of the trees resembled motionless pythons. The lianas were coiled up like green serpents. A breath of peril and treason rose from the ground and fell from the foliage. The stars were wide open, like flowers of flame.

"How beautiful it is, all that!"

It was the first time Joan had expressed such a sentiment. She was customarily as rebellious to admiration as to surprise and terror. Emotions shocked her. She considered them to be signs of weakness.

"It's beautiful, very beautiful. And that makes me think of things to which I've never paid any heed. Dirk, is there anything beyond death?"

I groaned, discontented. I don't like to talk about things I know nothing about.

"Do you think the clergyman was right when he said that there was another self, and that that second self doesn't die with the first?"

"You're annoying me, Joan."

"Too bad. I need to talk to someone this evening. I know full well that you won't understand me."

She stopped, her gaze lost. "It's not that I'm afraid. Oh no! But I'm wondering why I don't know such a simple thing. And I'm also wondering why no one in the world, neither the gravest clergymen nor the best physicians, has ever known such a simple thing. And it is, in sum, the only thing that has any importance. How can that be, Dirk?"

"How do I know?"

"Naturally, you don't. You're not intelligent, but if you were, it would be the same. Dirk, we've been hunting together for fifteen years. We've slept side by side. We've ended up resembling one another facially, as our souls resemble one another. You could certainly tell me a lie, but you wouldn't succeed in making me believe it. I understand you. You're not a bad man, and I'm not a bad woman. Oh, to be sure, we both have slightly heavy things on our conscience, you especially. As for me, I've only ever had one merit, which is to be a loyal and devoted hunting companion. Women are very good, in general. I haven't been good, Dirk, because I resemble a man too much."

"You're talking as if you were going to die, Joan. You're annoying and stupid."

"It's odd to see how alone one is when one is going to die. One must be very cold. I've never occupied myself with all that before this evening. One must be so frightfully alone when one goes Down There! Do you believe that one encounters anyone else on the way, other souls that have departed at the same time?"

"Shut up."

"And then, one must be very naked. No flesh, no bones. A mass without form or contours. One must float, like a cloud. That must be very disagreeable. And one no longer has a name. One is no longer Joan, the tiger-slayer and the wife of the Forest Devil. One isn't even anyone. One is something. One wanders like that, in the emptiness. One would like to be someone, to become someone again, to call oneself by a name, to put on a body again. One is very alone, and very naked, and very cold."

"Will you shut up, once and for all?"

"Yes, I'll shut up, because I've said what I had to say."

We returned to the camp. Joan went to fetch water in order to boil the saucepan, and didn't come back. An indeterminate amount of time went by.

I would have heard her cry out if she'd been attacked by the tigress, I thought. *Oh, the bitch. Is she cheating on me with a Hindu?*

Then I reflected that that was scarcely probable. Joan wasn't a sensual woman, and she was scornful of the indigenes.

We set off to search for her, taking the path that led to the river. Suddenly, Nursoo the shikari howled three times: "The tigress! The tigress! The tigress!"

. . . And I heard the horrible mewling of the beast and the crushing of bones under its jaws.

There was nothing to be done. I understood what had happened. The tigress, lying in ambush, had pounced on Joan and, sinking its claws into her breast, must have bitten her lips, which had prevented her from calling for help. Tigresses are as cunning as they're cruel, you see . . .

Anyway, my poor Joan was devoured. I regretted her for a long time, because she was an excellent hunting companion. I'm neither tender nor a coward, but as long as I live, I'll hear that mewling, simultaneously furious and satisfied, and the crushing of bones under the frightful jaws.

Paradoxical Chastity

HAZARD had taken me to Genoa. I'd been a guest of the city for three days, and the journey, difficult and slow, had not diminished my vigor and my courage at all. You'll understand my implication. Man is nothing but a dog in heat, a sage has said. In sum, nocturnal solitude was enervating me considerably. I resolved to find a temporary mistress.

One of my friends, to whom I confided my perplexity, offered to take me to the house of the procuress Myriam, who was famed for her genius for intrigue. Machiavelli herself would have admired her silently. She had the best choice of women and she understood her art royally.

Her palazzo was reputed to have a magical splendor.

I went with my friend to see the procuress. At the first glance I judged that my friend hadn't praised her dwelling stupidly. We climbed a staircase of the purest white marble, like a glacier. The sculptures of the bronze banisters represented quivering hamadryads inclining toward rivers and springs to listen to the murmur of naiads. Solemn statues illuminated the semi-darkness with their polished reflections.

Two Moorish servants preceded me into a vast room hung with dark red velvet. I observed the sculptures of the majestic mantelpiece. Immobile Vestals were watching over the hearth. The light struck a painting in which two huntresses were bringing to an image of Artemis the offering of their victorious bow.

The attenuated hues of the carpet evoked all of an extinct Persia. The vases of pottery, faience or sculpted metal were laborious miracles. They were worthy of flowers. A flamboyant summer of roses was consumed in perfumes. The immense bay windows overlooked the sea, which mirrored everything before our dazzled eyes, streaming with molten silver and speckled with crystal.

A woman came in. Never have I seen a more magnanimous beauty. The oriental magnificence of a beautiful Jewesses burst forth in her. Pale with ecstasy, I contemplated the red and blue glints in her black hair. Her eyes were the color of grapes. The red velvet of the curtains and hangings framed her with vivid flames and intensified the mat ardor of her flesh of amber and nard. Her mouth was like the fresh redness of watermelons.

That woman was living sumptuousness. She resembled a royal garden, an inestimable adornment, a fabric ingeniously embroidered by patient hands. Something grave and distant that was in her inspired, or rather, imposed, an involuntary respect.

My friend bowed deferentially. "This is one of my friends, Myriam," he said.

I stood there confounded. That creature, more beautiful than the most beautiful courtesan, was the procuress!

She smiled. Jezebel, powdered with gold and precious stones, must have smiled in the same immodest and regal fashion.

"You'll be dazzled, signor," she promised. She disappeared behind the red cloud of the curtains.

My companion was observing me curiously.

"But it's her that I want!" I exclaimed, drunk with admiration and stupor.

He shrugged his shoulders. "Refrain from turning your covetousness toward her," he advised. "She's as inaccessible as a summit of snow and ice."

"I didn't know you had that jesting humor, my friend."

"I'm not joking. Myriam is chaste. She's believed to be a virgin. She traffics the virtue of others while keeping her own intact. She knows the value of what others sell or give away too lightly. Then too, her profession must have inspired a horror and disgust for men in her. I repeat, don't think about it any longer."

Disdaining that stupid raillery, I uttered an exclamation of impatience.

At that moment the doors opened very wide, and a choir of young women, as rosy as the Graces, came in buzzing like a swarm of bees. The atmosphere was saturated with odors. But I only saw Myriam, a black sun amid the stars. I had never understood, sensed, or loved the proud prestige of brunettes with that profundity and that intensity.

"This is Myrto the Sicilian," said Myriam. "Her flesh has a scent of ripe apples. This is a flower of Spain, Violante. She's as beautiful as her name. And this is Lollia, who plays the guitar more adroitly than a Venetian, and Naïs, who dances like a Fauness. This is Nemea, as blonde as the gold of the sun."

"I adore blondes," enunciated my friend, "and this one is as bright as one could wish. What a whiteness of surf!"

137

He followed Nemea, who drew him away.

Myriam, seeing my lack of enthusiasm, for the feminine court, murmured in my ear: "If you aspire to someone more highly placed, I can introduce you to a Marchesa of a heroic lineage; but she demands an oath of absolute silence before the Madonna before taking off her mask. She's beautiful and poor."

I refused with a gesture.

"I divine your thinking. You're in love, and the lady is rebellious. Whisper the name of the indifferent individual to me, handsome cavalier. No one can distill the words that insinuate and persuade as well as I can. Unless she's as cold as a statue, I'll bring her to you in a few days. And if she persists in the frigidity of stone and snow, I'll find you a young woman in her image, who will resemble her feature for feature, but who will be milder and more docile to your desires."

I gazed at her fixedly. She had placed her hand on my arm, and that cool hand was burning me.

Myriam's voice had become even more flexible.

"I'd like to talk to you, to you alone," I interjected, abruptly.

She smiled with all of her brown face. "Go, my doves."

The gracious forms vanished.

I took a very rare ruby ring off my finger, as beautiful as the blood of a wounded woman, and I threw it, along with my heavy purse, on to the onyx table.

"Take them, Myriam. And also take this sapphire, of Mediterranean blue. In exchange, give me your most expert kisses."

She smiled again, but a sharper smile. "You're mistaken, signor," she replied, very calmly. "I'm the merchant, not the merchandise."

I met her haughty gaze.

"You're a coquette of the first order," I sniggered, "but you please me. All the gold you ask of me, I'll pour into the hollow of your hands."

"I sell others, but I don't sell myself."

Mad with desire, I drew her toward me.

"Love me, for I love you." And I imposed my feverish kiss on those cold lips.

She recoiled, and, extracting herself from my grip, she slapped me so violently that I tottered.

"Get out," she ordered.

But the vanity of the male protested within me, and I resolved to force that woman to submit to my will.

I approached her, my senses exasperated to the point of rape. My hands sought the wild breasts that were raised impetuously by an irritated breath.

More prompt than the flight of a swallow, she seized a stiletto, a marvel of niello and gemstones, which ornamented her belt, and plunged it into my breast.

I fell. An intense pain shot through my heart. I sank into the depths of a red night . . .

It was only with great difficulty that the most expert doctors snatched me back from the tenacious claws of Death. I was cured by a miracle of vigorous youth.

I did not cross again the threshold of the procuress, that strange, perverse and pure woman, immodest and inaccessible . . .

The Splendid Prostitute
(The Narration of an Envious Man)

$\ldots$ AND Glory appeared to me. I glimpsed her eyes, the color of bronze, and her hair, the color of blood. I was slightly surprised by that apparition, for I had scarcely hoped to profit from her fickle favors. But Glory is a woman—which is to say, cruel and perverse—and she loves to show off the spangles of her constellated skirt before those she disdains.

I stiffened myself, in order to contemplate her without amour, with all my pride and all my disdain. And I said, slowly: "My abode is not a hovel cluttered with bottles of nasty perfumes and pots of make-up. What have you come to do in this empty room, only furnished with memories? Why do you want to dazzle the Past that I am? I see you as you are. I've turned away from you, nauseated. You're the drunken mistress of thieves and acrobats. The odor of abattoirs pleases you and you aspire voluptuously to the precious odor of blood. You're as blind as those who make a profession out of judging their neighbor. You're as stupid as warriors and as venal as prostitutes. You abandon yourself for preference for those who violate you, and if, by chance, you exalt a proud woman or a poor man, it's merely a caprice of a drunken courtesan. In truth, your vagina is a public place, and I wouldn't want to welcome such an ugly whore into my modest bed."

"You're lying like a child," she replied. "I haven't the slightest intention of delivering myself to you. You know, in any case, that you'd pay for my mercenary kiss with your spilled blood. The stupid vanity of being talked about! But it possesses you as much as the others."

"And yet," I interjected, "it's a miserable joy to excite legends around one's person, the malevolence of which only equals their stupidity. Oh, the poisonous words that circulate in your veins and flow in your blood! You're even more of a calumniator than a cowardly denouncer of hidden faults. It's you who dishonor in secret all those you exalt in public."

"Perhaps you're right. But it's good, sentimental people who hope, by their writings and their works, to attract toward their solitude the fraternal souls of today and tomorrow."

"Those souls are fraternal because they remain unrevealed," I objected. "I have never encountered an individual on earth without later regretting having understood them too well and known them for too long."

"You're lying again, for I've seen a woman by your side whose indulgent mildness makes you weep with amour."

"It's you who's right this time. The man who encounters on his path an honest woman ought not to seek anything more or desire anything more. But what do my life and thoughts matter to you, the beaten servant of butchers and howlers of the stage? To you, who engrave in marble the insignificant names of kings and disdain the obscure names of good poets? To you, who places Hugo, the prince of the bourgeois, higher than Rimbaud and Charles Cros?

To you, finally, who allowed to perish the sacred songs of the Ionian Myrtis, the heroine Telesilla and, above all, the melodious and virginal Eranna of Telos? Even your servants have an unavowed scorn for your caresses. They return to their manuscript or their canvas with disgust; thus the dog of Writing returns to its vomit. Like opium-smokers and drunkards, they're damned by an incurable vice. In truth, go away . . .

"Night is falling, and also that of imminent Death. And the hope of a brief and painless death consoles those who are sitting in the dark . . ."

The Saurienne
(Narrated by Mike Watts)

THE sun is terrible. The sun is more terrible than the plague, the wild beasts and the gigantic black serpents. It is more terrible than the fever. It is a thousand times more terrible than death.

The sun has burned my nape and my temples and my cranium; it has desiccated and blanched my hair like the grass, during heat-waves. Another man than me would have gone mad after long marches in the desert. It seemed to me, at times, that molten lead was running over my brow and along my limbs. Ha ha! Another man than me would have gone mad, but I have a solid head and body. I've seen men howling and gesticulating like demons after long days of marching in the desert. The sun, hammering their imbecile brains, had given them strange ideas, But me, I've always been tranquil and reasonable.

The sun is terrible.

Toward the end of an afternoon, when long rays of light were still raining down, as sharp as javelins, I encountered a bizarre woman. I'm not a coward, but that woman scared me because of her frightful resemblance to a crocodile.

She had rough skin, like scales. Her little eyes frightened me. Her mouth frightened me even more, being immense, with sharp teeth, also immense. I tell you that the woman resembled a crocodile.

She was gazing at the water when I had the courage to approach her.

"What are you looking at?" I asked her, curious as well as slightly frightened.

She posed her terrible little saurian eyes upon me.[1] Instinctively, I recoiled.

"I'm looking at the crocodiles," she replied. "I'm somewhat akin to them. I know all their habits. I call them by their names. And they recognize me when I go along the river bank."

She was speaking in such a simple tone, so naturally, that I shivered with glacial fear. I knew that *she was telling the truth*. I dared not stare at her skin, as rough as scales.

"The king and the queen of the crocodiles are my intimate friends," she continued. "The king lives at Denderah. The queen, who is as powerful and even crueler than him, preferred to go forty leagues higher up, in order to reign alone. She wants power without division. He also likes independence, which means that, while remaining good friends, they live separately. They only come together at rare intervals, for the act of amour."

I saw a gleam of libidinous ferocity in her pupils, which made my teeth chatter. I'm employing that banal expression deliberately, all the force of which, and all the horror

---

1 The word *saurien* does not have the same implication in French as its English equivalent, referring to the order of reptiles that includes crocodiles, caimans, etc. rather than to dinosaurs, so a more literal translation would render this word as crocodilian and the artificial feminine derivative as crocodilienne, but it seemed more esthetically satisfactory to employ the transcriptions.

of which, I understood at that moment. The frightful sun was oppressing me and crushing me, like the weight of a giant. Liquid fire, it was burning me. And yet my teeth were chattering as if it were winter, when the great frosts make your blood torpid.

"I believe you," I panted.

She drew closer to me, with a gauche movement that was heavily insinuating . . .

The simpering of that monster was even more terrifying than her deformity.

"No, you don't believe me. What is your name?"

"My name is Mike Watts."

"Well, Mike, I affirm to you that I can ride crocodiles mounted on their backs. Do you believe me?"

I was sweating even more abundantly, but this time it was a cold sweat that chilled my limbs.

"Yes, I believe you."

And, in fact, I did believe her. I'm not mad. I've never been mad, even in the desert, even when I was thirsty. But I believed her, and you would have believed her, as I did.

She sniggered odiously—which is to say that she opened her mouth. She opened her abominable caiman's mouth very wide, and showed me her teeth, silently. A frisson caused her body to undulate, and that was all. Oh God who invented Hell!

"No, you don't believe me," said the Saurienne. "But I'll prove to you the truth of what I'm saying."

She scrutinized the yellow river, which was carrying sand and mud.

"Here's one," she said. "Stand back."

I didn't wait for her to reiterate the order. I ran away as fast as I could. Some distance from the river, however,

I stopped, suddenly fettered by something even more peremptory than fear.

At the moment when the crocodile unclenched its jaws I saw her hoisting herself up on to its back and, for the duration of a nightmare, I saw her riding on an alligator . . .

I'm not rambling. I have all my reason. Nor am I lying. Lies are for the civilized. We never lie. We hate complications.

The Saurienne came back toward me, leaving the crocodile thrashing around heavily in the brackish water. She came back, her eyes shining with triumph . . . and something else . . .

She was looking out for an exclamation of approving surprise. But I was tottering like a drunken man and stammering incoherent syllables . . . *ba . . . be . . . bou . . . bi . . .* And I was drooling like an idiot.

She looked at me with the libidinous and ferocious pupils of a monster in rut.

"Come," she commanded.

I tried to follow her. I could not. I made the strangled gestures of a lunatic restrained by a straitjacket.

A few paces from where we were there was a clump of very long grass, and trees whose branches resembled giant snakes. She squinted at that shelter from the corner of her eye. I had no difficulty divining what she wanted from me.

It would be difficult for me to explain to you what I experienced at that moment. All sorts of ideas were galloping through my brain, like an enraged dog-pack. I understood that it was necessary to kill the Monster, but how? How?

Bullets and blades would slide over her carapace without doing her any harm. Come on, isn't there even one vulnerable point? No . . . yes! The eyes . . . THE EYES!

I was seized by a joy of fever and delirium, the joy that is only known to shipwreck victims finally returned to land and invalids who see the dawn dissipating the night of their horrible hallucinations. I danced; I made my saliva hiss. I even stammered a few stupid amorous words to my redoubtable companion.

I emptied my water-bottle in a single draught. The thought of my imminent deliverance flowed through my veins with the beneficent warmth of brandy. I would thus have the strength to accomplish the murderous task . . .

And while the Saurienne, her gaze capsized beneath intoxicated eyelids, awaited the carnal satisfaction, I took my knife . . .

I took my knife and, striking the monster wallowing in the grass, I put out her eyes . . .

I put out her eyes, I tell you. Oh, that's because I'm courageous, me. You can complain on my account, but you can never claim that I'm a coward. Many men would have lost their head in my situation. Me, I didn't hesitate for a second . . .

And, as I went away, I turned round to see, one last time, the yellow river that was carrying sand and mud.

The Veil of Vashti

As innocent as Christ, who died for men,
she is devoted to women.
(Flaubert, *The Temptation of Saint Anthony*[1])

QUEEN VASHTI prepared a feast for the women of
the household of King Ahasuerus.[2]
The courtyard of the palace was as resplendent as a
sunset. The pavement of nacre and precious stones was
blooded with roses. The marble columns were garlanded
with daturas. Green blue and white drapes quivered around
golden beds, attached by ribbons of byssus cloth and silver
rings.

The feast lasted seven days. Slaves poured drinking water into variously sculpted malachite vases, and there was
an abundance of royal wine.

---

1 This line is spoken in Flaubert's novel by Simon Magus, with refer-
ence to his legendary companion Hélène, supposedly an incarnation
of Ennoia [Divine Thought].

2 This story is a dramatization of chapter 1 of the Biblical book of
Esther, with a feminist commentary added—as it was by various other
nineteenth-century writers referencing the story, including Harriet
Beecher Stowe, although Vivien's analogy with Lilith is original to her.
The king called Ahasuerus in *Esther* is generally thought to have been
Xerxes I.

On the seventh day, Vashti, surrounded by the princesses of Persia and Media and the wives of nobles and provincial governors was listening to the Musiciennes. They were singing the praises of the power and the wisdom of the queens of India, who have glaucous serpents for lovers.

Vashti's visage was as beautiful as the night. Her proud eyebrows designed a triumphal arch. Her eyelids were lowered, as solemn as the violet eyelids of Slumber. And her dark eyes, in which Ethiopia was radiant in its entirety, were vast unknown lands.

The Musiciennes fell silent. An old Jewish slave recounted the legend of Iblis and Lilith, who was created before Eve and was the First Woman.

". . . and Lilith, disdainful of the amour of man, preferred the enlacement of the Serpent. That is why Lilith has been chastised throughout the centuries. Some have seen her, in melancholy moonlight, weeping over dead serpents. She is like the supernatural dreams of solitaries. She torments the candor of slumber with dreams. She is Fever, she is Desire, and she is Perversity. In truth, Lilith has been chastised throughout the centuries, for nothing will ever satisfy her hunger for the Absolute."

"I would have done what Lilith did," thought Queen Vashti, aloud.

"Iblis, like his mortal companion, is accursed, O Sovereign, Iblis is the fallen star that sinks into darkness; for he dreamed of being the equal of God."

"I would have done what Lilith did," thought Queen Vashti, aloud.

"Iblis is the foremost of the vanquished, O Sovereign, for Iblis wanted the Impossible."

"I like the vanquished," murmured Vashti. "I also like those who attempt the Impossible."

The old Jewess, who had the knowledge of times, seemed to be collecting herself. Vashti shredded a pink lotus.

A thunder of laughter shook the marble columns and made the nacre and porphyry of the pavement tremble. It was the courtiers, intoxicated by the magnificence of the king. The king, whose court was rejoiced by wine, encouraged them.

Vashti lowered her eyelids in order to dissimulate the scorn in the depths of her Ethiopian pupils. Her limbs exhaled aromatics, the oil of myrrh and the perfumes in usage among women.

The green, white and blue drapes parted. Vashti covered her face with a gray veil gemmed with beryls, which resembled a marine dusk.

The seven eunuchs who served King Ahasuerus entered, their footfalls silent. The princesses of Persia and Media ceased their whispers and murmurs. The eunuchs knelt down at Queen Vashti's feet, and made the order of King Ahasuerus known to her. Vashti considered them through the gray veil with eyes similar to the bored eyes of lions.

In the silence that followed the messengers' words, one could have heard a rose shedding its petals.

"O Princesses of Persia and Media, King Ahasuerus has ordered Mehuman, Biztha, Harbona, Bigtha, Abagtha, Zethar and Carcas, the seven eunuchs who serve King Ahasuerus, to bring Queen Vashti into his presence, circled by the royal crown, in order to show her beauty to the people and the nobles . . ."

There was an anxious silence. That order from King Ahasuerus was, in truth, something that had no precedent in the history of the Medes and the Persians, or in the history of India or that of the Ethiopians; for the impure gaze of men ought not to profane the mystery of the feminine visage.

Vashti said, in a very slow voice:

"This is the response of Queen Vashti to King Ahasuerus: *When Queen Vashti received from the eunuchs the order of King Ahasuerus, Queen Vashti refused to come.*"

The eunuchs withdrew. All the faces had changed. One Persian princess dropped the cup from which she had been drinking, and the king's wine spread out over the porphyry and the nacre of the pavement. The king's wine spread out, as red as a pool of blood.

The old Jewess tore her robe and struck her breast "Woe betide you and us, O Queen!"

Rigid, like a marble statue with eyes of black stone, Vashti spoke thus to the princesses of Persia and Media: "I will not unveil my sacred face before a crowd of drunken courtiers. The impure gaze of men must not profane the mystery of my visage. The order of King Ahasuerus is an insult to my pride as a woman and a queen."

The old Jewess, seizing a cassolette in which perfumes were burning, covered her white head with ashes and lamented: "Rebellion is a deadly thing, O Queen! Think of the rebellion of Iblis. Think of the rebellion of Lilith. Think of the eternal chastisement of Lilith and Iblis."

"What does it matter?" said Queen Vashti, then. And she pronounced these solemn words: "It is not only in thinking about King Ahasuerus that I have acted. For my action will reach the knowledge of all women, and they will say: *King Ahasuerus had ordered that Queen Vashti be brought into his presence, and she did not go.* And from this day forward, the princesses of Persia and Media will know that they are no longer the servants of their husbands, and that a man is no longer the master in his house, but that a wife is free and a mistress equal to the master in her house."

The princesses of Persia and Media stood up and looked at one another with new eyes, in which the pride of the liberated individual was radiant.

The old Jewess was still lamenting . . .

The green, white and blue drapes parted for a second time, and the seven eunuchs of King Ahasuerus appeared again.

The seven eunuchs, Mehuman, Biztha, Harbona, Bigtha, Abagtha, Zethar and Carcas, spoke thus to Queen Vashti.

"O Queen Vashti, when the King heard the response of Queen Vashti to King Ahasuerus, the King was very irritated; he was inflamed by anger. Then the King addressed the seven sages who had the knowledge of times. He had with him Carschena, Schethar, Admatha, Tarsis, Meres, Marsena and Memucan, seven princes of Persia and Media, who see the face of the King and are the foremost in the kingdom. 'What law,' he said, 'is it necessary to apply to Queen Vashti for not having carried out what King Ahasuerus had ordered her to do by way of the eunuchs.'

"Memucan replied, before the King and the princes: 'It is not only with regard to the King that the Queen has acted badly, it is also toward all the princes and all the people who are in all the provinces of King Ahasuerus. For the action of the Queen will reach the knowledge of all wives and will lead them to disdain their husbands. They will say: *King Ahasuerus had ordered that Queen Vashti be brought into his presence, and she did not go.* And from this day forward, the princesses of Persia and Media, who have learned of the action of the Queen, will report it to all the king's chiefs, resulting in much scorn and anger. If the King thinks it good, let it be published on his behalf and let it be inscribed among the laws of the Persians and the Medes, with a prohibition of transgression, a royal ordinance after which Queen Vashti will no longer appear before King Ahasuerus and the King will give the dignity of Queen to another, who is better than her. The edict of the King will make it known throughout the kingdom how great he is, and all women will render honor to their husbands, from the greatest to the humblest.'

"This advice was approved by the King and the princes."

The princesses of Media and Persia wept silently.

Vashti stood up, and, with a haughty gesture, removed the royal crown from her hair. She also removed the pearls from her neck, the pale sapphires from her fingers, the beryls from her arms and the emeralds from her belt. She took off her robes of byssus cloth and purple, and put on the torn tunic of the old Jewess. Then she circled her forehead with pink lotuses and wrapped herself entirely in her crepuscular veil.

"Where are you going, Mistress?" sobbed the old Jewess, prostrate.

"I am going into the desert, where human beings are as free as lions."

"No man has ever returned from the desert, Mistress, and no woman has ever ventured into it."

"Perhaps I shall perish there of hunger. Perhaps I shall perish there under the claws of savage beasts. Perhaps I shall perish there of solitude. But since the rebellion of Lilith, I am the first free woman. My action will reach the knowledge of all women, and all those who are slaves in the hearth of their husband or their father will envy me in secret. Thinking of my glorious rebellion, they will say: 'Vashti disdained being queen in order to be free.'"

And Vashti went into the desert, where dead serpents come back to life in the moonlight.

As Brown as a Hazelnut

NELL was certainly an excellent companion in adventures. She was as brave, as vigorous, and more intelligent than a boy. I loved her very much and I wanted her to be my mistress; but she didn't want that.

Why not? How do I know, never having had the time to study women? Then again, women irritate me. I don't understand their behavior at all. I prefer wild beasts. At least they allow themselves to be captured, and, once one has captured them, that's it: they're caught, there's no going back. Whereas women, damn it, once one has them, it's necessary to keep them. And one can't keep them. Above all, one has to mistrust them when they say they love you. When they don't say anything to you, it might be that you please them, but even that isn't certain. When they tell you that they detest you, there's every chance that it isn't true, but perhaps it's also the involuntary confession of the secret hatred that every woman, consciously or unconsciously, harbors against men. There I go, talking like a book, and all in order to establish, in the final analysis, that with women, everything is possible and nothing is certain.

I'm not artful, myself. In consequence, I haven't been put inside as often as others, who were. It's necessary not to be artful with women. They always perceive it but, as they're stronger than you are, they make a semblance of not seeing anything. Then, without you knowing anything, they play a remarkable little comedy for you. And you're rolled over. For myself, I feel very sorry for men who boast about their feminine conquests, because they're bound to be cuckolded without knowing it, the poor fools.

Nell wasn't a true woman, and yet, she wasn't ugly. She had a lovely forehead and lovely eyelids. I like long hollow feet and long thin hands. I detest little feet inapt for interminable marches and little hands that can't handle a revolver or a carbine. Women, in general, are a great encumbrance. But Nell wasn't a true woman.

I don't know why she didn't want to be my mistress. We have no morality in the great woods. But she was refractory to amour. There are many women who have an instinctive horror of the male. It isn't that she had a profound hatred for me. On the contrary, she had promised me a fraternal affection. When I was wounded in the hand, she bandaged me up better than a nun. She even consoled me with all sorts of amicably gentle words.

"Poor old chap," she repeated, although I was only thirty then.

I'll never forget her eyes, as brown as hazelnuts, and her short hair the color of sand. I called her the Nut-Brown Maid, in memory of an old Scottish ballad.[1] She too was a maiden as brown as a hazelnut.

So, I was saying that she liked me a great deal, as a friend, a comrade and a hunting companion. But when I tried to make her share the sly desire that had gradually slid into my veins, I bumped into her rigid will, like an

---

1 "The Nut-Brown Maid" was collected by Thomas Percy in his *Reliques of Ancient English Poetry* (1765). It is not Scottish.

iron wall. At those moments, she considered me with such a grim horror in her gaze, such a repulsion in her entire being, suddenly hostile, that I had to beat a retreat. All that pleased her was the open air, marches through the forest, wildflowers picked on the way and the peril of the adventure. She was just as much made for peril and adventure as me. We liked one another as brothers. Beneath our amity, although it was real, was a corrupt mud of suspicion, even hatred. She didn't trust me, and I hadn't forgotten the ferocious resentment of a disdained male. Men are pigs, you see, simple pigs; moreover, that's their one superiority over women, who sometimes have the weakness, and make the mistake, of being good. I'll never forgive Nell for not having wanted to be my mistress. No, I'll never forgive her, even on my death-bed . . .

One incident, above all, vexed me. We were in the heart of the forest, in a very green twilight, when I tried to kiss her on the mouth. She planted a punch between my eyes so hard that I was disfigured for two weeks . . . two weeks during which my hunting comrades mocked me pitilessly. But that wasn't all. She added an insult to the physical injury she had caused.

"I'd rather swallow a toad that let myself be kissed by you," she said, pointing at the minuscule brown creature that had suggested that comparison, unflattering to my person.

An idea occurred to me, which was rather cowardly, I admit, but ingenious. In great pain, I devoted myself to a frantic chase, the result of which was the capture of the little toad.

"Swallow it right away," I ordered, "or I'll kiss you by force."

She looked me full in the face. Grave, she understood that I wasn't joking. An inexpressible scorn snaked over her thin lips, ascetic and eremitic lips. She took the frightful beast and swallowed it, only slightly pale.

That slight incident discouraged me. I didn't attempt to kiss her again. And I bore a mortal grudge against her.

One day, she came to me, her hazelnut eyes brighter and more joyful than usual.

"I have a superb project to submit to you, dear old Jerry. You know that I have an infinite affection for you, although I chose to swallow a toad rather than kiss you. I'm going to prove my amity by taking you with me this evening. We'll go out at dusk, in a boat. We'll take a torch to light the way, and the two of us will have a magnificent hunt by torchlight. We'll kill a great many deer before to-morrow morning."

"I'd like that," I acquiesced. And that same evening, we embarked in a boat that an old Indian lent to Nell.

What an unforgettable magnificence! The torchlight bloodied the water with scarlet reflections. One might have thought one was seeing a blazing palace in the water. The two banks stood out in blood-red. The trees were displaying red foliage, as in October. It was as beautiful as an Infernal landscape. Except that in the matter of the damned, there was only me. And I don't believe I'd committed a sin great enough to merit that splendid setting.

"Over there!" whispered Nell, imperiously.

With her extended finger she pointed at the right bank. I saw two large eyes reflecting the red light.

"A deer!" I exulted. I grabbed my rifle and, aiming between the luminous eyes, I fired.

We heard a rustle of leaves and reeds, and then the water was stirred by a heavy fall.

158

Nell uttered a cry of joy when we discovered a superb fallow deer on the surface, which I grabbed by the antlers and hauled triumphantly into the boat.

Nell picked up the paddle again and we went downriver in silence.

It was a beautiful yellow night. The darkness resembled thick layers of amber. The moonlight was streaming like a river of molten gold, and the stars were scintillating in the depths of the river like the spangles of a harlequin shirt.

Something stupidly sentimental was whimpering inside me. If the story of the toad hadn't still been running through my mind I would have loved Nell at that moment, with a passionate tenderness. I can't turn long phrases, but I would have taken her hand between mine, and I would have become better. I wouldn't any longer have had any anger or hatred against anyone. I would have forgiven the Indian who had stolen my silver watch. I would even have pardoned her for the stupid amour that she made me suffer. I would have become credulous and confident, like a little child. I would have done, for her and because of her, meritorious and disinterested things. I would have rendered services to people. I would have stopped fighting, even with the Tuscaroarers.[1] In order to get closer to her, I would have been as gentle as her. Yes, I would have stopped being brave in order to be good, and isn't that the greatest sacrifice that one can make for a woman?

In the shadows I glimpsed Nell's lovely forehead and lovely lowered eyelids. While justly calling myself an idiot, I sensed myself becoming as stupid as a book of poetry.

---

1 This spelling of Tuscaroras—an Amerindian tribe—does occur in a number of nineteenth-century American newspapers, so I have reproduced it as given.

The low voice of the Nut-Brown Maid interrupted my inept reverie.

"Those eyes that are looking at us through the bushes! Have you seen those eyes, Jerry?[1] They're not the eyes of a deer. They're shining in a very different fashion. Then again, they're smaller and closer together. Can you see them, out there? How they shone through the bushes!"

"You're right, Nell."

"Then too, see how they're moving. The eyes of deer don't move in that fashion. Deer don't move their heads in irregular circles, like that. Their gaze passes rapidly from one thing to another, or stares intently. Deer don't have those indecisive and blinking eyes, Jerry."

My rifle troubled the river and the night with brief small thunder.

"Don't shoot, imbecile!" Nell shouted at me.

But it was too late. The shot had been fired.

We looked toward the bank. To my great surprise, the eyes were still fixed on us through the bushes, but they were shining with a red gleam of anger.

I turned to Nell, awaiting an explanation of the enigma.

A furious porcine grunt reached us. I sensed myself go pale. Even the Nut-Brown Maid was slightly troubled.

We were dealing with a gray bear.

"Your bullet certainly hit it," Nell murmured. "As long as it doesn't attack us . . ."

A crackling of leaves . . . an abrupt and heavy plunge . . . Nell's fears were realized. The bear was swimming after us.

---

1 The original has "Dirk" at this point, although it is abundantly confirmed elsewhere that the narrator's name is Jerry, suggesting a momentary confusion with the narrator of "Treason in the Forest."

With all her strength and all her courage, Nell pushed the boat forward. We glided rapidly over the river, followed by the sniffing and snorting bear.

The nocturnal uncertainty enveloped us.

"If it catches up with us," said Nell, very calmly, the boat will capsize under its weight. It'll be necessary to swim, like the bear, and one of us will never reach the bank.

I had the very natural hope that it would be her. We were disarmed. Our rifles had fallen to the bottom of the boat and the water had put them out of action. And by a diabolical hazard, I couldn't find my knife.

I turned toward the young woman, whose paddle was cleaving the water untiringly. Suddenly, she straightened up with an anxious start.

"Listen, Jerry . . ."

Our apprehensive gazes met. We heard the sound of falling water.

"That must be the waterfall we heard higher up, at the river bend," I ventured.

"No . . . the sound of the water is close by. Jerry, Jerry, the waterfall is no more than a hundred meters away. Make use of the butt of your rifle as an oar and help me to stop the boat."

We succeeded in slowing the skiff down, and were hoping to steer it toward the bank when a heavy impact caused the rear of the boat to oscillate. The vacillating torchlight revealed the head and the long curved claws of the bear. The instability of the boat, which was dancing madly and threatening to turn upside down, didn't discourage the tenacious beast, but gave us a moment's respite.

Nell looked at me, with her indomitable eyes.

"Are you afraid, Jerry? Myself, I'm not afraid. This might be very brief . . . I've always had a great deal of affection for you, my brother Jerry . . ."

A surge of amour, as furious as despair, pushed me toward her.

"Since we're both going to die, my darling, my beloved . . . since we're going to die in ten minutes, in five minutes, perhaps three minutes . . . give me your lips. Let me kiss you on the mouth, and I'll die happier than I've lived. I'll even be content to die."

She was as hostilely pure as one of those little marine creatures that live stuck inside a seashell with nacre walls. I saw the dolorous contraction of her entire brown face.

"I can't, Jerry. Even before the great darkness, I can't. And yet, I love you dearly, my brother Jerry . . ."

That was more bitter than the idea of death. Certainly, I was grossly stupid that evening, beyond my custom.

She pulled herself together rapidly,

"All hope isn't lost, Jerry. It's necessary not to die without having fought Death."

I replied to her, with a discouraged gesture: "If we land, we'll fall under the claws of the bear . . . and if we don't land, the current will carry us over the waterfall. It might be very high . . . it might measure fifty, or even a hundred feet."

"In that case, let's head for the shore," Nell decided. "In the meantime, grab your rifle by the barrel and thump the bear's muzzle."

I obeyed, and we glided toward the shore. Suddenly, a crack resounded, more atrocious that a revolver shot fired next to the ear. I couldn't retain a scream of fear. Nell, as silent as Bravery, showed me the useless handle of the broken paddle.

"Swim!" I shouted.

"It's too late, Jerry . . ."

The current was carrying us irresistibly toward the waterfall.

Sitting in the dark and in the shadow of death, we looked at one another one last time. I would carry, all the way to the unknown, the bitterness of her stubborn refusal.

"Oh, how cold Death is!" Nell muttered.

. . . The horrible memory . . . ! The boat bounded forward. There was the abominable fall . . . the noise . . . the water . . . the foam . . . the spray . . . like smoke . . . the mist and vapor . . . darkness . . .

. . . And the awakening . . .

We were floating gently on very calm water. The thunder of the cataract was no more than an echo. Nell, her eyelids lowered, appeared to be collecting herself.

My head was spinning like a child's top. The stupor into which I was plunged resembled the dolorous distress of a hangover.

"Nell . . ." I called, very softly.

The lovely eyelids were raised slowly. I only found dazed eyes.

"It was only a small waterfall after all. If I had known! And the bear?"

We saw it through the yellow gloom swimming toward the bank. The shock of the unexpected fall had deflected its anger. It preferred to forsake its vengeance and head for the security of the shore.

"There are imbeciles who say that one only dies once, Jerry. For myself, I shall have known two agonies . . ."

Psappha Charms the Sirens

THE woman who incarnated my destiny, the woman who first revealed me to myself, took me by the hand. She took me by the hand and led me to the grotto where Psappha's songs charmed the Sirens.

In the same way that the Goddess once buried herself in the depths of the Venusberg and reigned there in spite of the different centuries and the changed world, so the Musiciennes took refuge in a grotto in the Mediterranean. The blue stalactites scintillate distantly there like cold stars. The sea murmurs around the rocks, whose tresses of green algae are dotted with anemones. A little foam breaks against the walls, more polished than marble.

"Come," said the virgin who incarnated my destiny. "But remember that those who enter this grotto never return to the land of the living.

"Like them, you will be eternally subject to the spell of the Past. The waves will muffle for you the distant bellowing of the multitude. The glaucous shadow of dusk will make you scorn the light of day. You will be a stranger to the race of men. Their joys will be unknown to you; their criticisms will be indifferent to you. You will be different, until the end of your human existence. You will be more dead than the radiant phantoms that will surround you, and which retain the confused survival of the Illustrious.

"Psappha will offer you the flower of her graces. Eranna will speak to you of Agatharchis and Myro. Nossus will weave her mauve irises for you. Telesilla will praise the value of heroines for you. Anyta will evoke in pastoral strophes the freshness of springs and the shadow of orchards. Moiro will disturb you with the enigma of her Byzantine gaze. The Past, more alive and more sonorous than the Present, will retain you in its silvery nets. You will be the captive of dreams and vanished harmonies. But you will respire the violets of Psappha and the crocuses of Eranna of Telos. You will contemplate the white peplums of virgins who bend over as they collect seashells as delicately mysterious as open vaginas. Sometimes, seated on a rock, they listen to the marine soul of conches. Toward evening, the Kitharedes will sing the songs of their homelands. Come."

And I heard a chord like the breeze that sighs through nocturnal pines at sunset . . .

My strange companion took me by the hand, and I followed her into the grotto where Psappha charmed the sirens.

The Club of the Damned

THE GLASGOW HELL CLUB, recounts an English author, Mrs. Crowe, in a curious volume entitled *The Night Side of Nature*,[1] was a fable of the good puritan city. Its orgies were severely criticized by the modern disciples of John Knox, who shook their respectable Scottish heads in chorus.

The Club of the Damned held its sessions every night. Those late nights were prolonged until first light. And the rare passers-by awake in the early twilight contemplated the illuminated windows of the Club while dissimulating a vague dread. The gleams were attenuated, spectrally, in the vast reproving clarity. Hoarse songs rose up in zig-zags, punctuated by drunken hiccups. And the horror of bursts of laughter fused, as sinister as kisses devoid of amour.

All that debauchery has of the abject and the crapulous was avidly sought by the members of the demonic Club. They were hated fearfully. They were scorned prudently. People stood aside from their insolent passage.

The most cynical of the Damned was Ninian Graham. That young Scot, who had neither talent nor a future, was

---

1 Catherine Crowe's *The Night-side of Nature; or, Ghosts and Ghost-seers*, was first published in 1848. The present story is a slightly modified version of a story told by Mrs. Crowe, whose protagonist is named as "Archibald B."

entangled in the pleasure of vice. When he had attained his majority he abandoned his studies for his mistresses, Barbara and Maggie, and, having been unable to choose between them, he ruined himself impartially for both of them.

One evening in November, Ninian headed for the mountains. His horse was valiantly following a rocky path that skirted an abyss when a stranger, who had been lying in ambush behind a spectral rock, launched himself into the road and seized the animal's bridle.

"Come!" he said to the young Scot, who was immobilized by an incomprehensible terror.

"Where are you taking me?" Ninian's voice finally quavered.

"To Hell!" replied the unknown man, of whom nothing could be seen but eyes as vast as the despair of darkness.

And the unknown man drew Ninian into the gulf . . .

They fell . . . they fell for an incalculable time.

The unknown man finally spoke: "We're nearly there."

Ninian expected ferocious clamors, blasphemies and the gnashing of teeth. His moist temples froze. His eyelids fluttered, and then closed over sightless pupils.

A murmur of voices woke him up from his miserable stupor. He opened his bewildered eyes violently.

He was in the home of his aunt, who had died five or six years before. The venerable old lady was knitting, while her guests of yore, an old naval officer, a retired businessman and his respectable wife, were playing bezique. Ninian recognized them all. A frisson shook him. They had the honest and blissful air that had been their principal attraction during their terrestrial existence.

"Where am I, then?" stammered the young man.

"In Hell," replied the old aunt, with simplicity. And she lowered her eyes over her work again, smiling.

An unspeakable horror insinuated itself into Ninian and bit him to the marrow. He ran to the door wildly, went down the stairs and hurled himself into the street.

The Presbyterian bells of a Scottish Sunday were chiming regularly. A crowd of well-dressed people were coming out of the church. There were fathers of families here, important patronesses of charitable endeavor, former grocers and magistrates. Young women were going by, their hair improbably smooth, holding well-disciplined children by the hand.

"Where am I, then?" Ninian asked one of those irreproachable wives.

"In Hell," she replied, in an assured and modest voice,

Ninian wandered through the populous streets for a long time. Dusk fell, ideally misty, and vesperal peace floated over the houses. The young man saw the red light of a tavern shining through the darkness. Men were drinking and singing. The whisky was gilded in their glasses, and the gin as silvery as moonlit water.

"Where am I, then?" he asked an old drunkard, who was cheerfully intoning an obscene refrain.

"In Hell, damn you," riposted the merry soul, with a loud laugh. His cordial appearance emboldened the traveler.

"People have always talked to me about Hell as a place of frightful tortures," he observed. "They were evidently mistaken, or, which is perhaps less probable, I'm mistaken myself."

"They weren't mistaken, and neither are you," the drunk interjected. "People are very cheerful in Hell. That's why they suffer so abominably there."

"But from what I can see," Ninian objected, "Everyone here is only reliving their terrestrial life."

"And that's the torture," replied the drunkard. He paused in order to swallow the contents of an enormous glass of sunlit eau-de-vie, and then continued, tearfully: "We were all souls devoid of amour and interest in the beyond. We only sought egotistical material satisfactions. So we're condemned to relive our past lives eternally. We retain, as before, a limpid gaze and a serene expression. We lead, as before, the satisfied existence of honest and worthy folk. And only we know what there is in our hearts and in our minds. We were the honest folk who, proud of their blameless past, judged the faults of our neighbors implacably. We were the worthy folk who, in their cozy placidity, remained insensible to the suffering of others. We were the worthy rapacious and voracious individuals whose fellows imitated them deferentially. We were the ferocious and stupid honest and worthy folk, and that's why we're condemned to eternal chastisement."

The drunkard's tears trickled down his violet-tinted cheeks.

He's maudlin drunk, thought Ninian.

The smoke was so thick that it veiled the blurred faces. Caught in the throat by the bitter emanations of alcohol, exhalations and sweat, Ninian was stifling. He vacillated on his legs, staggered and lurched . . .

He found himself on the moors, his head buried in the heather. His horse was grazing a few paces away. The morning air stung his temples and cheeks.

According to all evidence, the dream had been a presentiment of Heaven, since, a year and a day after that strange vision, Ninian Graham died—without, alas, having made amends.

The errors of his terrestrial life were such that we cannot hope for divine clemency for him. He could not—or, rather, did not want to—escape the Hell that had been so miraculously revealed to him.

Feminine Amity

OF all the lumpen stupidities with which the Philistines of letters overwhelm their readers, this is, I believe, the most formidable:

"Women are incapable of amity. There has never been a David and Jonathan among women."

Is it permissible for me to insinuate that the affection of David for Jonathan has always appeared to me to be more passionate than fraternal? I only require for evidence the young conqueror's funeral oration:

"You made all my pleasure. Your love for me was admirable, above the love of women."

I do not believe that those are the pale tears of dolorous amity. I rather recognize there the bloody tears of a widowed ardor.

How much more disinterested is the magnificent tenderness of Ruth the Moabite for Naomi! No carnal languor could slither into the amity of those two women. Naomi was no longer young. She said herself: "I am too old to marry again."

I know of nothing as beautiful, as simple and as poignant as this passage:

Naomi said to Ruth: Behold, your sister-in-law is gone back unto her people and unto her gods; return thou after thy sister-in-law.

And Ruth said: Intreat me not to leave thee, or to return from following after thee, for whither thou goest, I will go; and where thou lodgest, I will lodge; thy people shall be my people and thy God my God;

Where thou diest, will I die, and there will I be buried. The Lord do so to me, and more also, if ought but death part thee and me.[1]

Like the most beautiful music, those words leave you voiceless and breathless before the Infinite.

To the resigned offer of Naomi that the Almighty return the empty hands to the natal land, Ruth the Moabite responds with the phrase: "Intreat me not to leave thee, or to return from following after thee," which prepares, like a murmuring prelude, for the organ-like amplitude of the incomparable strophe: "Whither thou goest, I will go . . ."

Never has any amorous sob equaled that fervor or that abnegation. The poem of amity surpasses here the poem of amour. It is pure devotion, white passion. And that tenderness extends all the way to the tomb: "Where thou diest, will I die, and there will I be buried."

Naomi, whose name signifies beauty and tenderness, be honored for the amity that you inspired in your daughter-in-law, and which the daughters of Egypt celebrated thus: "Your daughter-in-law, who loves you, is worth more to you than seven sons . . ."

In truth, the Book of Ruth is the apotheosis of magnanimous amity. Amity: the chaste fusion of souls, snow melted in snow . . . amity: the sob of citharas and the perfume of violets . . .

Believe me, O Naomis and Ruths of the Future, what there is that is better and sweeter than amour is amity.

---

1 *Ruth* 1:15-17.

Svanhild
A One-Act Play in Prose

Scene I

The scene represents a shore of Nordfjord. In the background are mountains. Young women in peasant costume form moving groups. They are trampling bluebells, thyme and gentians underfoot. Motionless on a rock, Svanhild watches from a distance.

Thorunn: "What are you staring at, Svanhild? And for what are you waiting every day in silence?"

Svanhild: "I'm waiting for the return of the wild swans."

Gudrid: "You know full well that they have not returned to the country since the day of your birth. They stopped and reposed for a long time on the roof that sheltered you. So long as the light persisted they lingered on the roof of moss with blue and golden flowers, and, at dusk, they fled in a great flutter of wings."

Svanhild: "They'll come back."

Bergthora: "It was twenty years ago that they flew away northwards, and since that day, none of us has seen them pass over."

Svanhild: "I know they'll come back."

Bergthora: "Why do you remain standing on that rock, motionless and contemplative, for entire days?"

Svanhild: "I'm waiting for the return of the wild swans."

(*Festival songs are heard. Boats pass over the fjord, laden with women in bright costumes.*)

Peasant Women, singing:
> *Don't go near the glacier.*
> *For the cold burns like flame.*
> *Don't go near the snow,*
> *For snow blinds like the sun.*

(*They draw away.*)

> *Don't stay longer on the summits,*
> *For the azure attracts like vertigo.*
> *Don't contemplate the abyss,*
> *For the abyss attracts like water.*

Hildigunn: "Listen to that distant music. The boats are gliding over the fjord with a tranquil sway. The peasant women are rowing and singing; they're happy."

Svanhild: "Their happiness would be the worst anguish for me, and my happiness would be the bleakest torture for them."

Gudrid: "Don't you like anything on the earth?"

Svanhild: "I like the whiteness."

Thorinn: "What gift do you expect from life in its springtime?"

Svanhild: "Whiteness."

Ermentrude: "If destiny grants your wish miraculously, and the wild swans return, what will you do?"
Svanhild: "I'll follow them."
Bergthora: "How far will you follow them?"
Svanhild: "As far as the limits of the sunset."
Hildigunn: "What is the goal of your dream?"
Svanhild: "More whiteness."

Scene II

(A transient enters, her hands full of flowers, her head bare, her hair mingled with thyme and blades of grass.)

The Transient: "The roads are magnificently broad. I'm drunk on the dust of the road. I've slept in the heather, and though my dream, I've aspired the perfume of peaks. Red and violet berries have appeased my hunger, and melted snow has slaked my thirst. I've picked mountain roses. I've danced naked in the sunlight. Does anything exist under the azure of spring more beautiful than the lizards of the rocks, the blue and mauve thistles, the glimpsed scintillation of fish and the hues of the sky?"
Svanhild: "There is something more beautiful."
The Transient: "What can exist on the earth more beautiful?"
Svanhild: "Clouds, snow, smoke, foam."
The Transient: "Don't you want to follow, by my side, the road as free as the horizon and as vast as the dawn?"
Svanhild: "No."
The Transient: "Why?"
Svanhild: "I'm waiting for the return of the wild swans."

(*The Transient flees, joyfully.*)

Scene III

(*The setting sun illuminates the sky.
The evening is gray and pale.*)

Bergthora: "Here comes the dusk. How mysterious the mountains are!"

Gudrid: "How strange the silence is!"

Hildigunn: "The world seems to be waiting."

Svanhild (*to herself*): "Waiting . . . like me."

Thorunn: "Death lies in wait for those gone astray who linger in the mountains."

Asgerd: "The roads are perilous when the wind falls from the summits."

Svanhild (*with a great cry*): "The swans! The swans! The swans!"

All (*looking at the sky*): "We can't see anything."

Svanhild: "The North wind is blowing in their wings. They've crossed the sea, for the foam is silvering their plumage. They're heading for the open sea. Their wings are spread and quivering like sails. Can you hear the magnanimous beat of their wings?"

All: "We can only see the white clouds passing over the fjord."

Svanhild: "They're more beautiful than clouds. They're going toward the boreal lights. They're more beautiful than snow. How powerful and sonorous their flight is! Can you hear them passing?"

All: "We can only hear the evening breeze over the fjord."

Svanhild: "I'll follow them! I'll follow them to the limits of the sunset!"

Asgerd: "Svanhild! The roads are perilous when the mist falls from the summits."

Thorunn: Death lies in wait for those gone astray who linger in the mountains."

Gudrid: "Think of the fog that veils the abysms."

Svanhild: "O whiteness!" (*She flees into the depths of the mist.*)

Asgerd: "She'll get lost in the twilight."

Gudrid: "She'll perish in the night. Svanhild!"

All (*calling*): "Svanhild!"

The Echoes: "Svanhild!"

(*A loud scream is heard, reverberated by the echoes.*)

Gudrid (*anguished*): "The abysm . . ."

As White as the Foam

A S white as the foam on the gray of the rocks, Andromeda contemplated the sea, and the desire for Space was burning in her gaze.

Under the weight of golden chains, her delicate limbs were impregnated with sunlight. The wind from the sea blew through her outspread hair. The laughter of the sea went toward her, and all the dazzle of the shiny waves penetrated her soul.

She waited for Death; she waited, as white as the foam on the gray of the rocks.

She already felt lost in the infinite, mingled with the horizon, with the waves tinted with gold, with the distant mists, with all of the air and all the sonorous clarity. She had no fear of Death with chaste eyes and grave hands; she only feared Amour, who ravages the mind and the flesh.

As white as the foam on the gray of the rocks, she thought that the clement Gods, in delivering her virginal to virginal Death, were sparing her the rancors and pollutions of implacable Eros.

Suddenly, her dilated eyes fixed themselves on the Monster of the Sea that was coming from afar toward the motionless prey, toward the royal victim.

Its glaucous scales were streaming with blue and green water, and resplendent with flashes of radiance. It was magnificent and formidable; and its vast eyes had the profundity of the Ocean that lulled it with its rhythms and its songs.

From Andromeda's lips sprang a sob of fear and amour. Her eyelids fluttered before closing over the sensuality of her gaze. Her lips tasted the savor of Death bitterly.

But the hour of deliverance had sounded, and the Hero appeared, armed by Athena Parthene and like a bolt of summer lightning. The battle was joined over the waves, and the word of Perseus was victorious. The Monster sank slowly into the darkness of the water.

At the moment when the triumphant victor was about to break the Captive's golden chains, he stopped before the mute reproach of her tears.

And the voice of Andromeda sobbed, slowly: "Why did you not let me perish in the grandeur of Sacrifice? The beauty of my incomparable Destiny intoxicated me, and now you have stolen me from the Lethean kiss. O Perseus, know that the Monster of the Sea alone knew my sob of desire, and that Death appeared less somber to me than your imminent embrace."

Bona Dea

THE day is dying. It is the evening of spring consecrated to the Good Goddess.[1] Cover the image of my father with an impenetrable veil, in order that the gaze of the Immortal Virgin is not offended by the sight of a man.

Tonight, my father's house will be the temple in which the sacred rites will be accomplished . . .

How beautiful she is, the statue of the daughter of Faunus! Bona Dea, deign to lower your eyes with a smile upon our choirs and our offerings.

I have woven with my own hands the crown of violets that will circle your forehead. How vast and solemn your marble forehead is, O Goddess!

Here is the golden vase into which I have poured the wine of Lesbos. The wine is as luminous as the hair of Peitho. It is as red as the chlamys of Apollo. It will rejoice the dancing soul of enlaced women.

. . . Amata, thrice precious, close your beautiful eyelids,

---

1 The Roman goddess Bona Dea [Good Goddess] was only known by that nickname, or the alternative Feminea Dea [Women's Goddess], her true name being kept secret. The neoplatonist philosopher Macrobius opined that she was a version of the universal earth-goddess, worshiped as Fauna, Fatua or Oma, and that as Fauna she was the sister, consort or daughter of the ancient Greek God Faunus. Those data are reproduced in many nineteenth-century guides to mythology.

similar to dark flowers. Abandon your infantile hands to my ardent hands.

I love you. I, Caia Venantia Paullina, daughter of Cauis Venantius Paullinus, I love you, little Gaulish slave. You were only a paltry and graceless child, and the merchants disdained you, but I cherished you immediately and fervently for your lassitude and your fragility. I opened my arms to you; I wanted to console you as much as to embrace you . . .

For I am the being who dominates and protects; I love you with an imperious and tender love. I love you as a lover and as a sister. You will obey me, O my worry, but you will do with me whatever you wish. I will be both your master and your thing. I love you with the fury of a male desire and the languor of a feminine tenderness.

. . . I once opened my arms to you, as much to console you as to embrace you. Your shivering nudity, which I did not covet yet, charmed me by its candor. I loved you for being tremulous and for being frail. My strength was drawn toward your weakness; for I am the being who dominates and protects.

And now you are beautiful, Amata. Your breasts, like polished stones, are hard and cool to the touch. Your green eyes reflect the emerald foliage of oaks. The whiteness of your body has the transparency of mistletoe pearls. Your loose hair has the splendor of October forests.

And because you are beautiful, Amata, because you are the most gracious of adolescents, I will reveal to you the power and the sweetness of feminine amour.

I will teach you, if you deliver your consenting flesh to me, the multiple arts of Pleasure. I will teach you the savant slowness of hands that prolong their belated frictions. I will teach you the tenacity of lips that are delicately obstinate. You shall have the omnipotence of light caresses.

When you were still no more than a paltry and graceless child, I taught you the odes of Sappho the Lesbian, whose beautiful Dorian name is Psappha. Know, O my beautiful slave, that because I am your Priestess, Psappha, lying among the lotuses of Lethe, smiles when I invoke her and protect my amours. She will aid me to vanquish and retain your indecisive heart, Amata.

I love you as Psappha once loved Atthis, the fleeting and the uncertain.

. . . Because you are the most gracious of adolescents, Amata, I will reveal to you the power and the sweetness of the amour of women.

You are free, O my beautiful slave. This is the linen robe that I have woven for you. It is white, Amata, it is as attractive to the touch as your body itself. You are free. You can cross the threshold of this house, which protected your childhood. You can return to your homeland, without me addressing any criticism or reproach to you, without me darkening your joy with a lament.

For the amour of women does not resemble the amour of men. I love you for yourself and not for myself. I only want from you the smile of your lips and the radiance of your gaze.

Why am I beautiful to your eyes? For it is you who are beautiful and not me. My hair does not have the vesperal gold of your hair. My eyes do not have the distant clarity of your eyes. My lips do not have the sculpture of your lips. In truth, it is you who are beautiful and not me.

Never have I seen a virgin as desirable as you, O my lust, O my languor! Next to you, I am not beautiful. If a virgin more lovable pleases you more, possess her. I only want the smile of your lips.

I love you.

My pearls would be more luminous on your neck. My beryls would be more limpid on your arm. Take my necklaces. Also take my rings. Thus you will be ornamented for the festival of the Good Goddess.

She is simple and mild and merciful to women. She hates men, because men are ferocious and brutal. A man only loves his pride or his bestiality. He is neither just nor honest. He is only sincere in his vanity. And the Goddess is all verity and all justice. She is as full of pity as the water the refreshes the lips and the sun that refreshes the limbs. She is the clement Soul of the universe.

She it is who caused the first flowers to spring forth. Flowers are the work of the amour of the Good Goddess, the mark of her favor for mortals.

She only loves the faces of women. No man ought to soil with his presence the venerable temple where she renders her oracles. And the Priestesses alone have heard the divine sound of her voice.

She is the Daughter of Faunus. She is the prophetic and chaste Fauna. But her mysterious name, which must not be proffered by the profane lips of a man, I will tell you secretly: it is Oma. Do not divulge that sacred name.

The day is dying. It is the spring evening consecrated to the Good Goddess. The Vestals have garlanded with their chaste hands the walls that the foliage perfumes.

Might one not think it a motionless forest? The last gleams trail over your pale tresses. You resemble a Hamadryad framed with shadows and verdure . . .

The Vestals have garlanded with their chaste hands the walls that the foliage perfumes. They have chosen the simple flowers and the herbs dearest of all to Fauna: melilot, thyme, chervil, fennel and parsley. And here are hyacinths . . . here are roses . . .

182

The Good Goddess is happy with the joy of the universe. The pitying Nymphs serve and honor her, the Nymphs who, in feverish summers, bring in the hollows of their hands a water sweeter than honey . . .

The Goddess has colored the vermilion apple-trees. She has turned the virginal crocus of gardens blonde. She has turned the nocturnal blue of violets purple.

Fauna smiles at the amour of enlaced women. That is why, when night falls, the women will unite their lips before the beautiful statue that Theano the Greek has modeled expertly. The hair is solid gold, the limbs ivory and the eyes emeralds. But your hair is even more luminous, and your limbs more polished, and your eyes more profoundly green . . .

My fervent hands have circled the divine forehead with vine-branches. A serpent is coiled around the delicate feet . . . for she, who is Eternal Tenderness, is also Eternal Wisdom.

The wives who will come tonight have purified themselves by refusing the embrace of their husbands. But they are less dear to the Goddess than the sacred virgins.

Here comes the night, azured like the veil that protects the Divine Image, which must only be lifted by the hands of the Priestesses. For the Goddess is only unveiled on the spring evenings when the enlaced women unite piously.

Come, Amata, my beautiful slave. If you love me a little, you will accord me the kiss that my anxious lips await from your lips. You will bend to my willful embrace. You will abandon yourself to my imploring caress . . .

But I will not importune you with my desire or my tenderness, Beloved. I only want the smile of your lips . . .

CHRIST, APHRODITE AND MONSIEUR PÉPIN

Preface

Ibeg those who read me not to see in this little satire any irreverence to the divine Master Jesus Christ. The Occidental Messiah occupies a very high place in the hierarchy of my Gods. I love him and I venerate him with tenderness and profundity. What I am attacking in this minuscule volume is uniquely the mediocrity and the ugliness of the century, which would render the second coming of the Savior, although promised, impossible.

Once, the beautiful Syrian décor surrounded the Son of Man in his tranquil majesty: the Garden of Olives, the splendid desert, the temple of Solomon with its walls paneled with cedar and its golden altar. But today? If Christ reappeared among the pimps and prostitutes of Belleville and Ménilmont, how would he be welcomed by reporters?

Monsieur Alphonse Pépin, reporter for the *Grand Journal*, transcribes in these pages the origins of Christianity. He has seen. He has listened. A quotidian, almost mechanical scribe, paid without any great generosity, he registers and he establishes. Thousands of readers, unfolding the morning paper, see Jesus Christ with the eyes of Monsieur Pépin, hear him with his vulgar ears. The Gods only reveal themselves to souls worthy to contemplate them; and Jesus Christ, although the son of God and God himself, for Monsieur Pépin and the celebrated physicians he interviewed, could never be anything but "a vulgar madman afflicted by complicated megalomania and religious hysteria."

Let us be Christians; let us feel sorry for them rather than criticizing them.

Will I be accorded the favor of having the style, so personal and so particularly flavorsome, of Monsieur Pépin attributed to me? In all honesty, I cannot assume the credit for it, and consider it a duty to thank the anonymous collaborators from whom I have borrowed the turns of phrase most appropriate to translate exactly the beauty of our mores.

Christ

And lo, the star, which they saw in the east,
went before them, till it came and stood
over where the young child was.
(Matthew 2:9)

Unexplained Light
Opinion of Scientists. Ignaz Cornu.
The star of Bethlehem nothing but Juno

WE have solicited the opinion of competent special-
ist scientists on the subject of the strange celestial
phenomenon visible at present at Bethlehem.

Ignaz Cornu, the congenial director of the observatory
of Jerusalem, whom I went to see yesterday morning on
behalf of the *Grand Journal*, has received no other information than accounts that are somewhat confused and even
contradictory on certain points. He dismissed immediately
the hypothesis of a new star, comet or temporary star that
only the inhabitants of Bethlehem could see.

Monsieur Beaubois of the Institut, the distinguished as-
tronomer of the Observatory of Capharnaum, shares that
opinion completely. He is led to believe that it is nothing
but a very simple phenomenon immeasurably magnified
by the popular imagination.

Perhaps it is a matter, as was first supposed, of some new system of projection analogous to those tried in America for sending luminous advertisements all the way to the clouds.

Finally, Monsieur Ménage, with his habitual good grace, gave me another explanation, which seems to me to be the key to the enigma.

The phenomenon that is intriguing the inhabitants of Bethlehem so much is nothing but the planet Juno, which is shining in our sky at this moment with an incomparable brightness. Juno has, in fact, arrived at its perigee this year, a perigee that is only produced once every four hundred thousand years. It at such a point—Monsieur Cornu has observed it himself recently—that it sends us an appreciable light. One can even distinguish on a blank sheet of paper the shadow of a pencil that it illuminates.

The indications given by the observatories of Bethlehem, moreover, concur perfectly with regard to the time and the direction of the orbit described by the apparent present progress of that planet—I mean Juno, of course. The strange visitor adopts an ogival form. At this moment Juno is not at its full and, like the moon, affects the form of a crescent.

"This star is surrounded," Monsieur Cornu adds, "with a nebulosity that enables one to suppose that it is a matter of a planet, magnified by the reverberations of moist atmospheric layers."

That is what Monsieur Cornu tells us. Let us expect, therefore, to see the mystery that has thus far surrounded the Bethlehem apparition dissipate, unless it is a matter of a luminous projection that will one day be transformed into a simple commercial advertisement.

*

Jesus went up to Jerusalem,
And found in the temple those that sold
oxen and sheep and doves, and the
changers of money sitting;
And when he had made a scourge of small
cords, he drove them all out of the temple
and the sheep and the oxen; and poured
out the changers' money . . .
(*John* 2:13-15)

Scandal in a Church
Act of a Madman

The elegant audience that was listening peacefully yesterday morning to the sermon of Abbé Rossignol, curate of the Church of the Holy Sepulcher, on the necessity of contributing pious donations efficaciously, was painfully impressed at the moment of the collect by the inexplicable conduct of an unknown man whose disorderly conduct had been attracting attention for some minutes. The fanatic, armed with a whip made of rope, fell tooth and nail upon the beadle and the sacristan, and roughed them up so badly that one of them, Monsieur Cauchon, fifty-eight years old, an honorable father of a family, had to be taken to hospital. The police, whom someone went to fetch, arrived toward the end of the scene and had all the difficulty in the world mastering the lunatic, who was taken to the police station.

The madman immediately declared that his name was Jesus Christ, twenty-three years old, apprentice carpenter, of no fixed abode, the son of a victim of seduction, Mary, who had succeeded in marrying an honorable carpenter named Joseph, established in Bethlehem. He added that he was the Son of God and that he had been sent to earth in order to preach the good word to men and redeem their sins.

It is not known whether we are in the presence of a veritable madman or a skillful simulator. Pending more ample information, Jesus Christ has been confined to the special infirmary of the prison.

And it came to pass that when Jesus had finished these sayings he departed from Galilee, and came into the coasts of Judaea beyond Jordan; And great multitudes followed him; and he healed them there.
(*Matthew* 19:1-2)

The Country Messiah
Our Special Envoy in the Desert

For some time a certain Jesus Christ has been generating a good deal of talk. There is much rumor concerning the so-called miracles accomplished by his will. From the pretty village of Bethlehem, where he spent the first years of his life, the hundreds of invalids who have come to ask him to cure them have spread his name to the four corners of Palestine. The *Jordan Dispatch* has published a letter from a master fisherman, from which we have extracted the following passage:

"Jesus Christ, very well known in Jerusalem and in the surrounding areas of the desert where he spends part of the year, carries out numerous cures.

"In order to be cured, it is sufficient simply to have faith in him.

"The gentleman, only effecting his cures for humanitarian reasons and gratuitously, makes no effort to have his name appear in the newspapers. He has made more than five hundred people happy here, something that I can certify, having, as is commonly said, seen it with my own eyes."

Thus wrote the master fisherman.

Jesus Christ is, I am told, assailed daily by a host of invalids. That gives a good idea of popular confidence. I made the remark that no celebrated physician, no professor of our faculties only retailing the science acquired by his numerous works, in spite of all his notoriety, would ever have such a clientele.

I have conversed with various physicians who know Jesus Christ personally. They have affirmed to me that he is a good man, and, without wanting to explain his cures, they have recognized that he has obtained surprising results where science had failed.

The explanation that a celebrated alienist gave me is simpler:

"We find ourselves here in the presence of a vulgar alienated individual whose insanity presents known and catalogued symptoms: hallucinations, megalomania and religious hysteria. But this form of alienation is scarcely perceptible to crowds, especially mystical and superstitious rural crowds. It is not at all astonishing, therefore, that such a man can communicate his persuasion to crowds and operate by suggestion on maladies of nervous origin cures that are not outside the order of suggestions employed routinely in the treatment of neuroses. It is affirmed that he has cured blind people and paralytics, but there are cases of blindness and paralysis that are of purely nervous origin. One frequently finds oneself in the presence of such cases in hospices, which can be cured by simple suggestion."

And they began to accuse him, saying, we found this fellow perverting the nation, and forbidding to give tribute to Caesar, saying that he himself is Christ a King.
(*Luke* 23:2)

Troubles in Palestine
Situation Aggravated

It is absolutely undeniable that a strong mystico-revolutionary movement is operating at this moment throughout Palestine, where the socialist doctrines of the agitator Jesus Christ are unfortunately only too widespread.

The population is stirred up by the speeches of the exceedingly famous anarchist, and the worst disorders are feared in high places.

Jesus Christ preaches nothing less than the sharing of wealth, otherwise known as universal communism.

This man, endowed with a certain eloquence, has acquired an extraordinary and quite incomprehensible influence over the lower orders, and serious agitation is in preparation in rural areas.

We hope that our governor, Pontius Pilate, will show himself equal to the situation and will have the leader of the revolt arrested. It is necessary to make an example, all the more so as the audacity of the anarchist disciples of Jesus Christ, encouraged by the impunity, is increasing day by day.

We believe that it is our duty to signal to whoever has the right the veritable danger that is presented to public security by the formidable gathering of vagabonds, prostitutes, pimps and former convicts in the outskirts of Jerusalem. That disreputable crowd meets every day on the mountain in order to listen to anarchist speeches pronounced by Jesus Christ. Afterwards, all these apaches spread through the streets of Jerusalem repeating the seditious words they have just heard to all and sundry.

It is high time to put an end to this scandal. Let us hope that the police will soon decide to take energetic measures to safeguard the peaceful citizens who are justly anxious about the proximity of that horde of bandits.

Therefore they sought again to take him:
but he escaped out of their hands.
(*John* 10:38)

Flight of Anarchist Jesus
The Search Continues

The research undertaken by the security services to discover the anarchist Jesus Christ has not had any result. The deputy head of the Sûreté has, as we have said, circulated descriptions everywhere, but no response has yet reached the palace of Pontius Pilate. There is nevertheless every expectation that the dangerous anarchist, of whom the police possess a complete description, will be arrested before long. The police have set their finest sleuths on his track.

✳

And in the evening he cometh with the twelve.
And as they sat and did eat, Jesus said, Verily
I say unto you, One of you which eateth with
me shall betray me.
(Mark 14:17-18)

Then Simon Peter having a sword drew it, and
smote the high priest's servant, and cut off his
right ear. The servant's name was Malchus.
(John 18:10)

Arrest of the Anarchist Jesus
Sensational Capture

In accordance with the indications of the anarchist Judas, who had denounced the machinations of the leader of the gang, Jesus Christ, Monsieur Perdreau, the local commissaire and Inspectors Fromanet and Ravigotte, accompanied by several uniformed police, went to the Garden of Olives.

After having the exits covered by the agents, Monsieur Perdreau and the uniformed officers went into the Garden and conducted a veritable manhunt.

In truth, the capture was a perilous operation, for a man named Peter, forty years old, who was a member of the gang, had no sooner recognized the quality of the agents than he flew into a violent rage, threatening to kill them if they approached Jesus Christ. And so saying, he brandished a dagger with a sharp blade.

Without allowing himself to be intimidated by his resistance, the agent Malchus advanced and threw himself upon him. A terrible hand-to-hand struggle ensued, in the course of which the brave policeman had his ear cut off. The wretched apache, finally brought down, was handcuffed and taken to the commissariat, along with Jesus Christ, the instigator of that unspeakable act.

> *Now Peter sat without in the palace: and a*
> *damsel came unto him, saying, Thou also*
> *wast with Jesus of Galilee.*
> *But he denied before them all, saying,*
> *I know not what thou sayest.*
> (*Matthew* 26:69-70)

Interrogation of the Anarchist Peter
Sensational Revelations. New Details.
Moving confrontation

Before Judas, Monsieur Tantinet had interrogated the anarchist Peter, accused of affiliation to an association of malefactors, in the presence of Monsieur Jasmin, the amiable local Commissaire. Peter declared that he reproved propaganda by action and was not in relations with Jesus Christ. The agent Sale was introduced. He declared without hesitation that he recognized Peter.

Peter opposed an energetic denial to the agent's statement. Immediately, a superb cock, carried by a peasant who had been brought to the court in a state of complete inebriation, started to crow. The accused, moved, for reasons unknown, by the voice of the fowl, dissolved in tears, and Monsieur Tantinet was obliged to suspend the interrogation.

※

But they cried out, Away with him . . .
crucify him . . .
Then delivered he him therefore unto them
to be crucified. And they took Jesus
and led him away.
And he, bearing his cross went forth into
a place called the place of a skull . . .
After this, Jesus knowing that all things were
now accomplished, that the scripture might be
fulfilled, saith, I thirst.
Now there was set a vessel full of vinegar:
and they filled a sponge with vinegar, and
put it upon hyssop, and put it to his mouth.
When Jesus therefore had received the vinegar,
he said, It is finished: and he bowed his head
and gave up the ghost.
(*John* 19: 15-17, 28-30)

The Guillotine on Calvary
Execution of the anarchist Jesus Christ. Calvary

By dispatch from our special envoy:

Rarely does a criminal give proof before the scaffold of the firmness displayed by Jesus Christ, the man whose head fell under the executioner's blade yesterday morning in one of the public squares of Jerusalem.

Everyone knows that Jesus Christ had been condemned to death for having been the instigator of the recent troubles that have cost the lives of more than a thousand people.

The wood of justice sent from Rome had arrived the day before at twenty past noon at the Jerusalem railway station, and the news of the execution had spread rapidly through the city and the surrounding villages, so curiosity-seekers had flocked from all directions. In any case, the execution had already been expected for some time, and every day a numerous and noisy crowd had assembled before the prison howling cries of death. Those cries the condemned man had heard in his cell.

In the expectation of the imminent execution, large posters bearing the words WINDOWS FOR HIRE were covering the walls of the buildings overlooking the prison. There had been no shortage of takers, and, thanks to the location, the residents of the buildings had made considerable profits. Every night for a week, until an advanced hour, a swarming and noisy crowd massed at those windows had been awaiting the macabre spectacle impatiently.[1]

For three or four days, seeing nothing happen, those who had, in exchange for rather large sums, retained their places there, wondered anxiously whether they might be cheated and whether the execution was really going to take place there. This time, however, there was no doubt. The wagon had just stopped at the prison door. Already, the aides were seizing the uprights of the machine and plant-

---

1 All Paris still remembered vividly in 1907 the inglorious circumstances surrounding the public execution of the murderer Henri Pranzini, in August 1887, which was postponed several times, keeping an avid crowd waiting for a week; every window overlooking the Place de La Roquette had been hired out to the spectators, who stuck to their posts religiously throughout. Public executions were still being carried out, albeit with greater promptness, when the story was written.

ing them in the ground scarcely fifteen meters from the houses whose windows were at a premium.

At those windows there were men, women, children, little girls, even babies in their mothers' arms, and all eyes were extended toward the things being unpacked in the night, and which fell to the ground with a dull sound. All the way to the roofs, human clusters were suspended.

Everyone is satisfied; they will not miss a mouthful of the spectacle. So, from all parts, cries go up: "Bravo! Bravo! Hurrah for Pontius Pilate!"

In the adjacent streets, the crowd never ceases to grow. But the police orders are very severe. Brigades of gendarmes come from all points of the region, in anticipation of possible trouble, an artillery battery, an infantry regiment, agents of the municipal police and neighboring towns, bar all the streets giving access to the place of execution, into which only rare privileged individuals furnished with special passes by the court are admitted, along with the judiciary authorities.

The Awakening

Meanwhile, the erection of the sinister machine is progressing. In the buildings opposite the prison people are weary of watching, and through the wide open windows pass songs, laughter and joyful sounds. Here, guitars sustain some Spanish serenade, there a piano picks out a waltz, and couples can be seen twirling. Elsewhere, around laden tables, people are feasting while, sitting on a chair with a napkin on her head, a woman is singing a maudlin sentimental ballad. Outside, in the square, the dull sound of the mallets that are finishing setting up the guillotine punctuate the melodies. Cries go up:

"Death to Jesus Christ! To death!"

The hour of expiation is fixed for a quarter to four.

The Expiation

First light has blanched the sky. It is already daylight. At a slow pace, the wagon heads from the prison toward the guillotine, next to which it soon stops. The door opens, and the condemned man, supported by two aides, appears.

At that moment, an immense clamor goes up from the nearby streets: "To death! To death!" howl thousands of lungs.

A rapid pallor pales the cheeks of Jesus Christ, who turns round and lets fall the words: "Father, forgive them, for they know not what they do."

But the aides have just pushed him toward the seesaw, which lowers and slides toward the crescent. And as his neck is engaged within it, while the first aide, who had gripped his ears, pulls the head toward him, the condemned man clamors again in a loud voice: "Father, I commend my spirit to your hands."

A dry click. A flash. A jet of blood. The head falls into the basket. Justice is done.

And the angel answered and said unto the
women . . .
Go quickly and tell his disciples that he is
risen from the dead . . .
(Matthew 28:5,7)

Theft of a Cadaver
Mystery in a Laboratory

An audacious theft of a cadaver has just taken place in the laboratory of Dr. Beaubois, who had been sent the body of the anarchist Jesus Christ, executed yesterday on the Mount of Calvary, for the purpose of autopsy.

This morning, the expert practitioner was not a little surprised to see that the cadaver had been removed by unknown hands. The authors of this strange crime are being actively sought. Joseph of Arimathea, a disciple of the defunct anarchist and a prostitute, Mary of Magdala, known as Mary Magdalen, who was also closely associated with Jesus Christ, were arrested immediately, but have had to be released for lack of evidence. Mary Magdalen was able to furnish an alibi, which was recognized as sound. As for Joseph of Arimathea, the police were able to take account of the fact that his denials were expressions of the truth.

The most curious aspect of this bizarre affair is the belief in the special society of apaches and streetwalkers the late Jesus Christ habitually frequented that the famous anarchist has been resuscitated . . .

Aphrodite

GOLDEN APHRODITE, Kypris crowned with violets, was born a second time; for she wanted the multitude of human beings to rejoice in her presence.

Divinely naked, the Goddess sprang from the sea, and there was a universal hymn in the glad universe.

Lying in an immense conch with iridescent walls, rocked by the eddies, Kytherea sailed toward Paris.

Darkness had descended over a Northern landscape that the eyes of the Anadyomene no longer recognized. Noisy and pointed poplars, oaks and maples had replaced the olive groves and cypresses. The cicadas were no longer singing in the warm shadows. Golden peas were no longer flourishing on the river banks . . .

All night long, the Goddess floated on the river, and toward dawn, the conch stopped.

Kypris saw for the first time a city with gray stone bridges.

The Place de la Concorde awoke. And the Goddess, finally stopping, quit the traveling conch.

As naked as the day of her divine birth, Kytherea traversed the square and entered the city.

The morning breeze heightened the brightness of the starfish that crowned the forehead of the Goddess. A little spray still moistened the flower of her left breast. Her hair resembled a marine forest of golden algae. The variable irises of her eyes harbored all the colors of the sea. Whiter than the natal foam, the Olympian body was resplendent

As naked as the day of her divine birth, Kytherea entered the city . . .

And there was alarm and scandal among the passers-by. A senator, taking refuge behind his abruptly-opened umbrella said loudly: "Can one conceive such an outrage to public decency?" His reflection was aggravated, even more bitterly: "And naturally, not a policeman in sight!"

A concupiscent bourgeois let fall the words: "Damn, she's pretty, that little woman! Perhaps the waist isn't delicate enough . . . and the buttocks are somewhat lacking . . . but all in all, she's rather well-proportioned. Eh, little mother?"

Dragging her little daughter, whom she was taking to a music lesson, a blushing mother declared that Paris was no longer an abode tolerable for honest women. "Sluts like that, who go about the streets without a chemise, ought to be thrown in prison!" she exclaimed. Modestly, she added: "And in broad daylight too!"

Slyly, an apprentice butcher pinched the Goddess's rump. A gamin threw stones at her.

Serenely, Golden Aphrodite marched through the hostile, mocking, frightened crowd. The immortal's footfalls generated perfumes. Around her, the sunlight became very soft.

The senator, however, had departed at a run. He soon came back with two policemen, who took possession of the daughter of Zeus. And, having covered her with their regulation capes, they took her to the nearest police station.

When the commissaire summoned her, in an official tone, to state her name and occupation, the Goddess replied:

"Don't you recognize me, insensate? I'm Aphrodite, who loves smiles, Aphrodite, crowned with gold. I alone gave the Gods sweet desire. I tamed the races of humans and birds, and the multitude of savage beasts. Everything is the concern of Kytherea of the beautiful hair.

"Now listen and remember my words. I have quit the dwelling of my father, the wide Ouranos,[1] in order to pour for humans nectar mingled with delight.

"For the second time, I am appearing among mortals, not in maritime Kupros but in fluvial Paris . . .

"Stranger, have a temple built for me in this city that I have honored among all, where perfect hecatombs can be offered to me. I shall dwell there, amid incense and the perfume of woven garlands. Future races will bring me splendid presents and I shall receive the beautiful sacrifices of the Parisians, joyful in my spirit."

Thus spoke the daughter of Zeus, remembering the words of an Aede who had once praised her in irreproachable strophes.

The commissaire listened gravely. Then he gave an order in a low voice.

One of the agents immediately went out.

There was a pause, interrupted by the arrival of two uniformed officers. A fiacre was waiting outside the door of the commissariat. With a firmness exempt from gentleness the agents took hold of the immortal and threw her into it. Mysteriously, one of them communicated the address of the Depot to the apoplectic coachman.

Kypris with the resplendent cheeks was taken to a narrow cell. After a few utterly useless remarks, she was left in solitude.

---

1 Ouranos, in this context, is to be construed literally, as the sky.

The Blissful sat down, thoughtfully. In vain she had quit Ouranos beaten by the winds, the glorious abode of her father. Times and peoples had changed in a lamentable fashion. No one in the well-constructed city to which Kypris had come had saluted her or reached out to her. No one had recognized the immortal Goddess in his heart.

Dusk had fallen. Agents appeared again.

Taking possession of the Goddess again, they put her into a fiacre. The vehicle departed, limping along, toward a lunatic asylum. It jolted, grated and came to a halt, as if regretfully. The Goddess and the agents got down. Without a word, they traversed the courtyard.

But now the bars of a window framed a livid face. Haggard eyes were burning in that livid face, open with an immense stupor. And a hoarse voice uttered a heart-rending cry:

"I see you and I adore you, Aphrodite, born of the foam, immortal Kytherea! I contemplate you, light of Kypros, splendor of Hellas of the beautiful women! Be praised eternally, daughter of the sky and the sea, Aphrodite crowned with violets!"

With drool on his lips, the man fell backwards. A warder promptly imprisoned his convulsed limbs in a straitjacket.

The madman had been a poet.

At a tranquil pace, the Goddess entered the house. Above the roof, the chimneys of which were vomiting black smoke, a mysterious flock of doves suddenly soared, and in the fissures of the courtyard, roses sprang forth irresistibly.

But no one around the Goddess was witness to that suave prodigy because darkness had fallen in the courtyard . . .

Lightning Source UK Ltd.
Milton Keynes UK
UKHW04f1028220718
326088UK00001B/159/P